# Runkle Mapping Method - South America ©Brenda Runkle

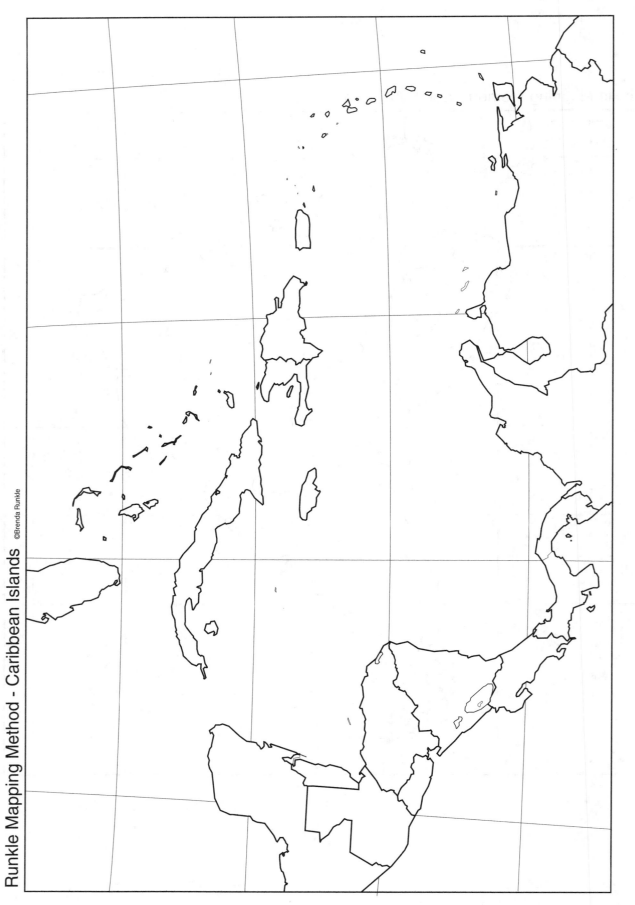

Runkle Mapping Method - Caribbean Islands ©Brenda Runkle

Runkle Mapping Method - Australia ©Brenda Runkle

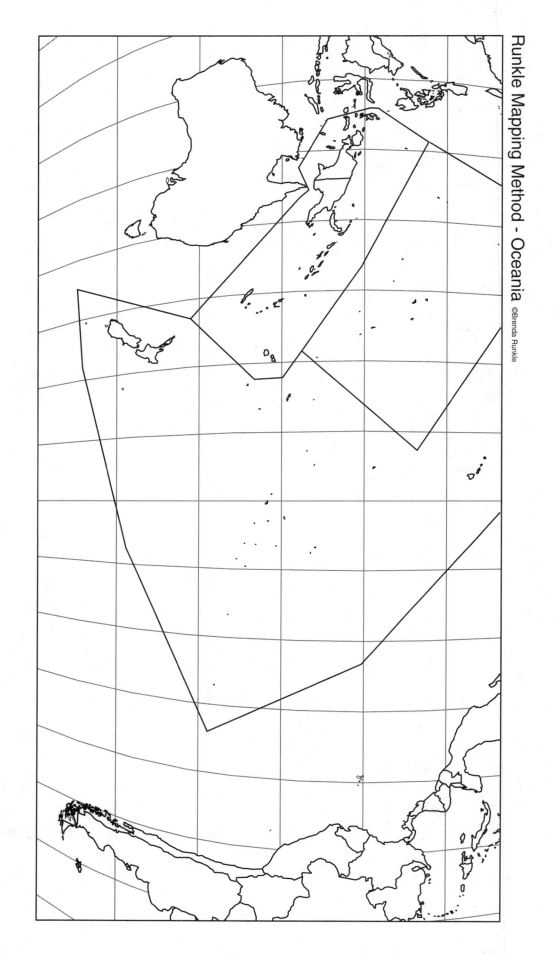

# Welcome to the Wonderful World of

# Geography

## WORLD PHYSICAL GEOGRAPHY

Student Activity Workbook

# Welcome to the Wonderful World of Geography
## WORLD PHYSICAL GEOGRAPHY
Student Activity Workbook

**Author**
*Brenda Brewer Runkle*

**Editor**
*Gaye Anthony*

**Consulting teachers**
*Rita Baker, Kings Mountain Middle School, Kings Mountain, North Carolina*
*Chuck Claxton, Boddie Middle School, Milledgeville, Georgia*
*Terry Coffey, Chamberlin Middle School, Fairview, Oklahoma*
*Chris Combs, Okeene High School, Okeene, Oklahoma*
*Stephanie Davis, Kings Mountain Middle School, Kings Mountain, North Carolina*
*Howard Hinish, Everett Middle School, Everett, Pennsylvania*
*Tony Hurt, Boddie Middle School, Milledgeville, Georgia*
*Ron James, Almont Junior High, Almont, Michigan*
*Tracie Kitchens, Boddie Middle School, Milledgeville, Georgia*
*Tammy Price, Chamberlin Middle School, Fairview, Oklahoma*
*Chuck Puckett, Baldwin Middle School, Milledgeville, Georgia*
*Reese Todd, Oklahoma City Community College, Oklahoma City, Oklahoma*
*Elise Walker, Boddie Middle School, Milledgeville, Georgia*
*Cheryl Weaver, Boddie Middle School, Milledgeville, Georgia*
*Joyce Williamson, Boddie Middle School, Milledgeville, Georgia*

Cover photo by Lowe Runkle II

ISBN 0-9701112-2-3

Special note of appreciation to Sue and Dave Huettner and Frances Sanger.

**Runkle Publishers, Inc.**
P.O. Box 1363
Norman, Oklahoma 73070
e-mail: info@runklepub.com
Visit us on the web at www.runklepub.com

Printed in the United States of America by Quebecor World, Dubuque, Iowa

# Table of Contents

# South America

# Australia

# Oceania

# Islands

# Outline Map Masters

# Welcome to the Runkle Mapping Method

Thank you for buying my geography program. This workbook and the associated textbook are the result of over 10 years of student and teacher input plus hard work on the part of my staff and me. It has been a labor of love. I would like to take this opportunity to dedicate this first book to the memory of the late John Saxon.

*Our goal is...*

Our goal is to produce successful students. As adults we know a task must be repeated time and time again until it becomes second nature to us. My mapping method stresses this belief. It is very structured and uses all four methods of learning. Not all students learn in the same manner, so we address the complete range of learning styles. Students will read, speak, listen and manipulate on a daily basis.

*The text is...*

The text is written in individual lessons, making it easy to plan a day's or week's activities. Starting and stopping points can be easily determined. The text is also conversational, addressing the students, asking them questions, reminding them of other lessons, and asking for interpretation of information. There are very few unassociated facts.

The story of geography is woven like a tapestry. It all goes together to form a most intriguing story. Our Earth is so interesting. One goal is for the students to travel down the highway not playing video games, but looking out the windows thinking about what they see. What kind of climate is here? How does one region change into another? How has the land been changed to meet the needs of the people there? Are these trees indigenous to this climate? Are farmers trying to grow a crop here that really doesn't belong? Is the land being eroded by agricultural or industrial use? How has this road changed the lay of the land? How has it changed the character of the community around it? Why is this town here, at this particular location? Why did this city thrive and the one down the road become a ghost town? Are these people like those in my community or are they different? Are there any regional specialities such as okra in the grocery stores? How are the houses built? Is there a regional architecture? Do the houses in Seattle look like those in Boston? So much to think about!

*Fun, silly ways to learn...*

I use a lot of mnemonics, which are fun, silly ways of remembering things. For instance did you know that "very cold elephants prefer chile"? They do if you are learning the countries of South America!

*Continent by continent by continent...*

Each continent or area comes with a written text and a series of maps. My wish is for the student to know the countries, their capitals, correct spelling and relative location, plus important physical features such as natural boundaries. We introduce rivers as natural boundaries in the map series. When you study World Physical Geography you will discover other natural boundaries.

*Don't panic, now!*

You, as the parent or teacher, do not have to have all this knowledge in the beginning. Learn along with your students! Love of learning should be a lifelong experience!

*What else do I need?*

This program was designed to be used without any additional materials. However, I always recommend a globe, atlas and almanac simply because they are good teaching tools!

Welcome to the wonderful world of geography.

Brenda Runkle, Author

# Runkle Mapping Method

The purpose of this workbook is to help your student learn all the countries of the world, spell them correctly and place them in their correct relative location. It is not designed to be used page by page with the textbook. Included are detailed specific learning activities to assist you in using the maps in conjunction with the text. These activities are accomplished by using incremental memorization. The workbook will stand alone, although it is written to be used with the textbook. The outline map masters may be used to strengthen and reinforce the text with hands-on activities such as drawing in all the deserts of the world and identifying the countries that lie within each desert.

I suggest you spend 15 minutes or so each day in the memorization of the countries. There is a written text for you to follow that has mnemonics, fun facts and learning tips for each continent.

Please begin with Africa, as it is the most difficult, most unfamiliar and the one the students will take the most pride in mastering. Let me walk you through Africa.

**Map #1** puts Africa in its correct relative location by identifying the bodies of water touching its shores and where it is in relation to the equator, prime meridian and other continents or countries.

**Map #2** is a pretest. There is never a grade for a pretest. It is simply to let us know where we are as we begin a task. Do not be surprised if your students have little or no knowledge of Africa. Most people cannot name more than one country for the whole continent!

Next we go to the written text and **Map #3**. Follow your written instructions as to the number of countries to learn at one time and in which order they go. Remember this is incremental learning. Your first test will have only 5 countries, but your second test will have 10, then the third will have 15, etc. Always grade on spelling. I take off half of the assigned value of a country if the name is misspelled. Have your student write the name correctly at least 10 times, then give back the lost points. Do not rush. Our goal is to achieve mastery. We want them to be able to find each country in their mind's eye without a prompt of any kind.

There are four learning modalities, or four ways in which we learn. We see, hear, speak and manipulate in order to learn. When you do the lessons as written, you have met all the learning styles and each child should be able to achieve mastery. Manipulation is the strongest learning modality. So encourage your students to trace, draw, color, label and cut out at every opportunity.

This workbook was designed to help you have at least two grades per week. You should have one map test grade and one text grade each week. It is easier to have each test worth 100 points, with the harder, longer tests worth 200 or more points. This is called "weighting the tests" to reflect difficulty. Assign value to questions as you see fit.

**Map #4** gives you the capitals of each country. This is not a required step. I include them just so your students can become familiar with the names. This will be a reference tool for you if you ever need to look up all the capitals. When our African embassies were bombed, the news media only mentioned the cities, not the countries. If your students can place the city on a continent, then it will be easier to find.

**Map # 5** asks the students to look at the maps and see if they can determine where a river forms a boundary. This step is important as it increases powers of observation. Although we have been looking at this same map for weeks, did we really see where the boundaries are?

I am a firm believer in the importance of fresh water. Today 3 out of every 4 people on the face of the earth do not have access to clean, fresh water. Thus, it is imperative for us to know where water forms a boundary, serves as a major transportation link or as a source of hydroelectric power.

**Map # 6** identifies the rivers. The students do not have to memorize each river. Once again, we just want them to recognize the name and be able to find the relative location in their mind's eye. Notice that important lakes are also listed.

**Map # 7** is the final test for Africa. You will be surprised and pleased with the ease your students will have using my method of mental mapping. It is so thrilling to close your eyes and be able to name all the countries in Africa. It is even more thrilling to close your eyes and find every country in the world. That gives you big-time bragging rights!

Students should not draw on the shaded maps. Use the outline map masters for any activities. As maps change, go to our website at www.runklepub.com and download the new maps or email us and we will send you a new one for whatever our cost is to reproduce and mail it.

Each group of maps follows the same pattern as those of Africa. I suggest you run off multiple copies of the outline map masters before beginning. Have the students color in and label each country as it is learned. Have your students cut out all the countries. We have to use common sense here. Do not expect them to cut out the very small countries individually, but include them with a larger country. Then toss the pieces on a table and tell them to put the continent back together. When they can do this they have achieved real mastery!

Be sure to periodically throw out the puzzle pieces for reinforcement. Just because you have mastered it once does not mean you will retain the knowledge without using it!

As you progress through the text, I recommend using multiple copies of the outline map masters for hands-on activities. For instance, as you identify the deserts of the world, have your students draw them in and name the countries they include. You may want to draw in the volcanoes, or the tectonic plates, etc. You may want to make separate maps for each, then take a long hard look and visualize how they go together. Please feel free to make as many copies as you need.

Although this workbook does not follow the text page by page, I hope you can see how important it is to learn the continents and countries while studying World Physical Geography. After you have finished World Physical Geography and move on to North America Physical and Cultural Geography, you will understand just how important it is to learn all the states before beginning an in-depth study of a continent. I will not stop and review, but will forge ahead on the assumption that you have followed my directions. This is how we will cover so much material so well in such a short period of time. (Our children really should know all the state capitals as well as those of Canada.)

Thank you for buying my products. Please feel free to contact me with any corrections, suggestions or information you wish to pass along.

Brenda Runkle

# Specific Learning Activities

As I travel around the country and get to know parents and teachers better, I am constantly asked for very specific directions as for the use of the maps with the text. Well, here it is, finally.

I am going to leave timing up to you, the teacher. Some lessons can be finished in 45 minutes or so. Others have numerous activities and will take longer. A rule of thumb is that when eyes glaze over you are wasting your time! Go on to something else and come back later. Incorporate geography with your history. If you are studying Alexander the Great, then get out a world map and plot his routes, etc.

## Chapter 1: Our Planet Earth

**Lesson 1** does not have a map activity for the solar system. However, you could have your students go to the library, research the subject, then draw a map of the solar system or, better still, make a diorama. This could be counted as an extra credit activity.

**Lesson 2** already has a map activity. If you have access to a copier this activity will be much easier than having to trace the continents from the book. Compare these continents, which were taken from a globe, to those on the Robinson, Mercator and Winkle projections in the map packets to better understand distortion.

**Lesson 3** is a continuation of Lesson 2. One of our goals is to be able to place countries and cities in their relative location all over the globe. For instance, did you know that Minneapolis, Minnesota and Venice, Italy are both located at 45° N? Paris, France and Vancouver, British Columbia are at 49° N while Grand Forks, North Dakota is at 48° N. What do you see in your mind's eye when you visualize these cities? Grand Forks is bitterly cold due to its location in the interior of the continent, while the climates of Paris and Vancouver are moderated by large bodies of water. As you work with these maps, ask yourself questions about location, climate, land use, etc. and you will be surprised at how much you already know about these things.

**Lesson 4.** Use one of the world maps and label all the oceans. Have your students rank the oceans as to size. You might also use an almanac and find more information as to temperature, salinity, depth, etc. Compare the size of the oceans to the continents as well. How many continents would fit into the Pacific Ocean? How many into the Atlantic, etc.? This will give you a good idea as to the land/water ratio of our planet.

## Chapter 2: Maps and Their Uses

**Lesson 5** has its own map activity.

**Lesson 6** has its own map activity.

**Lesson 7** has its own map activity.

## Chapter 3: Latitude and Climate

**Lesson 8** already has an activity, but you may take a world projection and mark increments of latitude. Keep doing this until you have it completely ingrained that there are only 90° of latitude. You will never see 110° N because there are only 90° of latitude.

**Lesson 9.** Use the same map as in Lesson 8 and add the low, middle and high latitudes, the Arctic Circle, the Antarctic Circle, and the tropics of Cancer and Capricorn. Use an atlas and mark the major cities located along the tropic of Cancer and the tropic of Capricorn, as well as the equator. Notice there are no cities in Antarctica and very few villages in the Arctic Circle. Think about the 24-hour days and the 24-hour nights and how you would adapt your lifestyle. Note that most of the cities of the world are located in the middle latitudes. Could that be due to the growing seasons, climate, and available water? Why do you think this is so? Each time you work with a map think about what you are doing and ask yourself questions. This is a wonderful way of learning.

**Lesson 10.** No map activity.

## Chapter 4: Prime Time Longitude

**Lesson 11.** You need to pay attention here because if you use a world map centered on Europe and Africa, the prime meridian will run right through the center and the 180° meridian will be on both outside edges. Remember, together the 180° meridian and the prime meridian form a great circle. Individually each covers only 180° of latitude. If your map is centered on North and South America, then the prime meridian will be to the east and 180° meridian to the west. Many people use the terms 180° meridian and International Date Line interchangeably, but the IDL does not follow the 180° meridian for its entire length.

**Lesson 12.** If you would like to have another hands-on activity, use a world map and have your student draw in all the time zones, paying close attention to the areas that use sun time. You could also draw in the cities in the Critical Thinking Activity on page 61 and then draw a line between the cities, with Los Angeles as your central point. Label time as you go. It is so important to be able to visualize time zones. Once I flew into Oklahoma from Florida and almost immediately got on a plane for Alaska. Well, when I went to Florida the time was one hour ahead of Oklahoma. When I went to Salt Lake City it was one hour later than Oklahoma time. My son and I were eating a leisurely breakfast when I glanced at my watch, set of course on Florida time, and immediately thought we had missed our plane. We went flying through the airport only to find out we had another hour before our plane left. I sure felt dumb!

**Lesson 13.** Follow directions in the book. Use one of the world maps and fill in the hours, then march around the globe changing days and hours as you go. Pick the longitude of your city, then see what time it is in Paris, France or Chicago, Illinois or any other town of interest to you. Use an almanac or atlas to find the latitude and longitude of the cities you are using.

## Chapter 5: Journey to the Center of the Earth (The Lithosphere)

I want to take this opportunity to stress that plate tectonics, subduction, and obduction are all *theories* at this point in time. Many scientists believe they are on the right track with these theories, just as many other scientists believe in the Biblical six days of creation.

**Lesson 14.** Here is a fun activity to do. You can either make salt dough or buy play dough. Read the text carefully to determine the size of each of the layers of the earth. Now, choose yellow for the center and follow the color sequence as shown in the book to make a ball. How big a ball? Well, that is part of the fun of this activity. You may have to redo your ball several times to get it right. When we are finished we will use dental floss to cut our earth in half. We want to see the layers in correct sequence and size. You will be impressed with the thinness of our lithosphere!

**Lesson 15.** Take a world map and draw in the margins of seafloor spreading in the Atlantic Ocean. Notice how it passes through the middle of Iceland. You might want to go to the library and look at the National Geographic articles on Iceland. It is quite amazing to see those volcanic fissures lighting up the night.

**Lessons 16 and 17.** Now this is a fun but somewhat difficult activity. We are going to draw our own map of plate outlines. Let's begin by darkening the outlines of the continents on a world projection of your choice. I always use a projection centered on the Atlantic Ocean. Now turn to page 82 and look at Fig. 5-13. You will have to look closely to determine the outlines of the continents. The outlines of the tectonic plates are not going to match the continents, so take your time and do this accurately. Be sure to place the California coast on the Pacific plate. Notice where Africa is going to split apart along the Great Rift Valley, as shown in Fig. 5-20. Remember that the triangles point in the direction of the subducting plate. For example, the Pacific plate is subducting or being pulled beneath the North American plate and forming the Aleutian Islands.

Pay close attention to the location of volcanoes and earthquakes (fig. 5-14). Find South America. Notice that loop of earthquakes and volcanoes to the east of the southernmost tip of South America. The loop follows the boundaries of the Scotia Plate. As these mountains rise above the surface of the water they will interrupt the continuous flow of cold water surrounding Antarctica. Then, gradually over time, Antarctica will warm and the ice will melt as warm waters wash her shores.

## Chapter 6: Mountain Building

**Lesson 18.** Let's do some complicated work here. Go back to Chapter 5 and look at Fig. 5-13 and Fig. 5-14 once again. Now draw in the continental shields (Fig. 6-2), and you will find they fit together quite nicely with the earthquakes and volcanoes. The shields are the oldest parts of the continents and will have little if any tectonic activity.

Now take a world map and draw in the Ring of Fire. Isn't it fascinating how the mountains, volcanoes, earthquakes and subduction zones form a true ring of fire around the Pacific? When something subducts it disappears, so we can deduce the Pacific Ocean is getting smaller as it subducts beneath the surrounding plates. We know the Atlantic Ocean is getting bigger as the mid-Atlantic Ridge pours forth new magma, moving the plates farther and farther apart. And so the dance of the continents continues!

**Lesson 19.** Take your world map and label each of the mountain ranges according to how it was formed. For instance, the Andes were formed by subduction, while the Urals, Himalayas and Rockies were formed by collision. The mountains in the middle of the oceans formed over hot spots. Here is an easy way to understand how Mt. Whitney formed. Take a book and place it on a table. Open the front cover and notice the steep angle as you open it. The distance between the pages of the book and the front cover represent the face or steepest side of Mt. Whitney. The sloping back side represents the slope of the mountain itself. Can you imagine the force necessary to raise such a huge slab of earth at that angle!

**Lesson 20** has a map activity to identify 30 famous volcanoes. There is a marvelous film called "In the Shadow of Vesuvius" that explains the eruption that destroyed Pompeii in 79 A.D. It is truly worth the effort to locate it! Try your local school board or library. This is especially timely as Vesuvius is making noises again!

# Chapter 7: The Hydrosphere

**Lesson 21.** No map activity.

**Lesson 22.** Pay close attention to Fig. 7-10 and Fig. 7-13. You should be able to see where the most rain falls and how most of the world's deserts are along the west sides of continents, in the interior of a continent or in the rain shadow of a mountain range. Of course deserts are also found at the high latitudes due to the freezing temperatures and lack of precipitation. Remember to name the countries or states lying within a desert.

Go back to your map of deserts and draw in the areas of upwelling. These are areas of dense, cold waters that are full of fish and always along the western side of a continent. They also represent areas of desert along the continental coasts. Draw in the ocean currents, once again noticing that north of the equator they move in a clockwise direction, while in the southern hemisphere they move in a counter-clockwise direction. The warmer waters will always be at the equator. The Benguela Current flows along the western coast of Africa, while the Peru Current flows along the western coast of South America. Some maps will refer to the Peru Current as the Humboldt Current.

**Lesson 23.** Continue using the same map from Lesson 22 and identify sandy deserts and those of desert pavements. Pay close attention to how many of these are in Arab countries. Locate the Gobi and Takla Maklan Deserts on your map as well.

**Lesson 24.** Use a map of North America and an atlas to identify the major rivers flowing east from the Rocky Mountains into the Gulf of Mexico, and then the rivers flowing west into the Pacific Ocean or Gulf of California.

**Lesson 25.** No map activity.

**Lesson 26** continues to use the map of North America. Pay close attention to the rivers, their headwaters and mouths. Name the states each river touches.

**Lesson 27.** Use your map of Mexico and Central America as well as the map of South America. Label the rivers and name the countries they pass through.

**Lesson 28.** Now come the rivers of Africa and Asia. Once again pay close attention to the headwaters of the rivers and their mouths. Mark them on you map, please. Label each country touched by these rivers.

**Lesson 29** is the rivers of Europe. Follow the same pattern and locate the rivers, find their headwaters and mouths and label the countries they touch. Work with this map until you can mentally map the boundaries of these important rivers. The Rhine and the Loire are especially important. Do more rivers flow to the north or to the south?

**Lesson 30** uses the map of Australia, a small continent with not many rivers.

**Lesson 31** has its own map activity.

**Lesson 32.** Use your map of the United States and trace the route of the Tennessee River. See how it joins with the Ohio and then flows into the Mississippi? It is marked clearly on page 150 in the textbook. Use a world map and mark out the route German u-boats would travel in order to sink Chilean ships. Do you think the German submarines passed through the Panama Canal? Did the Chilean ships use the canal to reach our eastern seaboard?

**Lesson 33.** You have already used a world map to draw in the cold ocean currents and the corresponding deserts on the continents. You should be familiar with the cold current alongside Peru known as the Peru or Humboldt Current. You should have labeled the Benguela Current along the western side of Africa. Both of these currents bring waters northward from Antarctica. Now it is important to draw in the areas of upwelling, the cold ocean currents and deserts and tie all of this information together. After you have finished with this map you will be able to draw conclusions about the relationships between these factors.

**Lesson 34.** No map activity.

## Chapter 8: The Atmosphere

**Lesson 35.** Watch the weather channel for several evenings and keep track of weather conditions. Use a map of North America to mark the low-pressure areas and high-pressure areas. Each evening mark how far they have moved and try to predict where they will meet. This is a fun activity to do for every season. You can see how the pressure ridges move. Compare December and May. Then compare July and March. You will really see some tremendous changes!

**Lesson 36.** Use a world map and draw in the horse latitudes, the doldrums and the trade winds and mark their latitudes. Follow the latitude of the doldrums around the globe and label large areas of population. Do many people live at this latitude?

**Lesson 37.** No map activity.

**Lesson 38.** Use a map of Africa and locate Mt. Kilimanjaro.

**Lesson 39.** Use a map of North America and draw in the Sierra Madre Occidental along the western coast of Mexico. Draw in the Sierra Madre Oriental along the eastern coast. Now, locate Mexico City at about 19° N 99° W. This is a region of high plateaus, with mountains to the east and west. Mexico City has an elevation in excess of one mile due to the elevation of this plateau. Remember, we have prevailing westerlies in the Northern Hemisphere, so the winds will drop their moisture on the western sides and weaken as they descend down the eastern slope. Once the winds flow into the valley, they have to rise again to get out of the valley. These weak winds cannot remove the industrial and automobile pollution. Mexico City is a very beautiful, old city but one plagued with foul air, tremendous overcrowding and poverty. Mexico is what we call an emerging nation. These countries lack a middle class. Most of the wealth is held by a small minority, and most of the people are very poor. The rise of a middle class spreads the wealth among people who have an education, a skill and a good job. The key to a middle class is having a skill that can command a good wage.

## Chapter 9: The Biosphere

**Lesson 40.** Why don't you do an extra credit activity here and research the Dust Bowl? Take a map of North America and draw in the outline of the Dust Bowl. Label the states involved. You might do some research on the role of the steel-tipped plow in digging up the matted roots of the grasses on the plains. It was the roots that held the soil in place, and as the grasses were removed and rains failed, the soil was left bare to blow away. Why did they have "mud rain" in New Jersey? Can you explain why and how that happened?

Do some research on desalinization. The important thing to understand about desalinization is that you must have a source of energy to boil the water in order to remove the salt. If a country does not have a cheap source of energy, then it cannot afford to desalinate water for any purpose. You might also want to look into the different kinds of irrigation and report on them.

**Lesson 41.** This will be a fun lesson. Use a world map and draw in the rain forests of the world. Now keep in mind that although there may be hundreds of inches of rain, many of the trees will actually be dying of thirst. Why don't you study animals of the rain forests? Or better still, research the problems in Brazil with the destruction of the Amazon Rain Forest. It is important to understand what is going on there because Brazil represents one of the largest labor pools in the world outside of China. Why are they destroying a forest that everyone recognizes as important to the global climate and clean air? Trees breathe in carbon dioxide and exhale oxygen. Why then are they cutting down this vital forest? This study will involve economics, cultural migration patterns, farming techniques, poverty, exploding population growth and many other factors. You will learn so much that when you study South America you will be well on your way to understanding their problems.

As you move along in this study notice how there is a mirror image of climates. What you have on one side of the equator, you have on the other. The only difference is the amount of land in the Northern Hemisphere and the lack of land in the Southern Hemisphere.

Did you understand that a highland climate can be found anywhere on the earth and is determined by elevation, not latitude? That is an important concept.

**Lesson 42.** You can continue your study of land use here and use a world map to draw in areas of deserts and desertification. This is a wonderful subject to do extra work on because it involves so many aspects of culture, history, economics and migration patterns. For instance, in many of the African countries cattle and goats are considered to be a sign of wealth. The more animals a man has, the wealthier he is. However, the more animals he has, the more damage they do to the land, making it impossible to support his animals in the first place. So, pick an African country and research the land use and spread of the desert.

Another interesting project would be to study the Aswan High Dam in Egypt and its effects on the Nile delta and agriculture.

Deforestation of the Himalayas is another interesting subject. But budget your time and do these activities as time and interest allows.

**Lesson 43.** There is no map activity here but you might want to take a world map and trace the route of the potato from North America to Ireland. Or you might want to do some research on tobacco, rice, tomatoes, etc. and trace their route of origin to other countries where they have become common.

**Lesson 44.** This is our last lesson. By now you have dozens of maps you have made yourself. You should easily be able to discuss where and why you think Jack grew his magical beanstalk!

# World Maps

Whenever you look at a world map, remember that the cartographer, or mapmaker, is trying to draw a three-dimensional object, the earth, on a two-dimensional piece of paper. The earth is a sphere and has height, width and depth. Paper has only height and width. This means all flat maps will be distorted and will not be accurate representations of the earth. The only accurate representation of the earth is a globe.

## Runkle Mapping Method ©Brenda Runkle

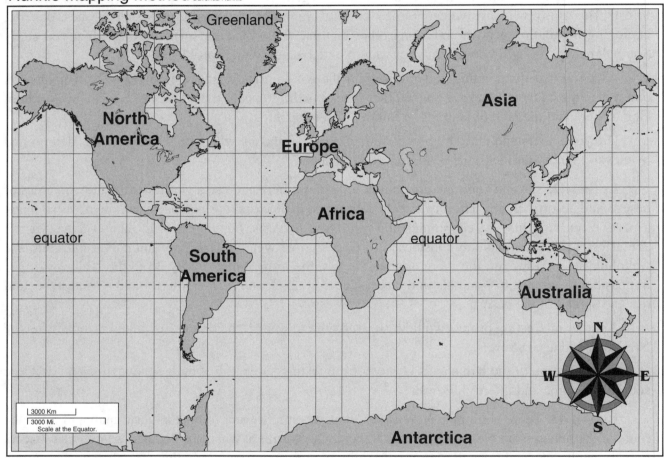

©1995 Cartesia Software

## Mercator Projection

This is a conformal projection, meaning it conforms to or maintains the true shape of the land masses. The land sizes change dramatically the farther away you get from the equator. Look at how large Greenland seems in comparison to South America. In reality, it would take 8.2 Greenlands to equal the size of South America! Notice the size of the grid boxes along the equator and those toward the bottom and top of the map. The boxes farthest north and south are quite large, yet represent the same area as the smaller boxes at the equator. This is a form of distortion. Gerhardus Mercator, a Flemish cartographer, drew this map in 1538. It remained the map standard for over 400 years.

The continents in order of actual size from largest to smallest are: Asia, Africa, North America, South America, Antarctica, Europe, and Australia.

10

Runkle Mapping Method ©Brenda Runkle

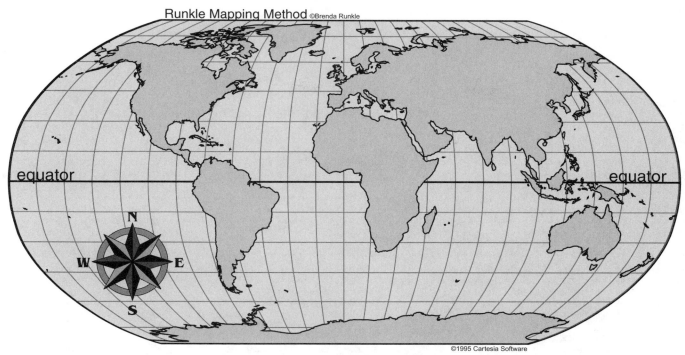

©1995 Cartesia Software

## Robinson World Map centered on Europe

These are Robinson World maps. Notice they are oval rather than rectangular, like the Mercator map. The grid boxes are not square nor do they form right angles. Continents nearest the equator, in the middle of the maps, will have the most accurate shape. The farther away from the equator, the greater the distortion. This means the greatest distortion will be at the edges of the maps. That is why Greenland appears larger than it really is and why Antarctica is spread clear across the bottom of the map. These are forms of distortion. Wavy mirrors that make you look funny are also forms of distortion.

The top map is centered on Europe and Africa. The one below is centered on North and South America. Notice how Asia is divided and appears at both edges of this map. We are able to see all of the Atlantic and the Pacific, but do not have a good view of Asia.

## Robinson World Map centered on the Americas

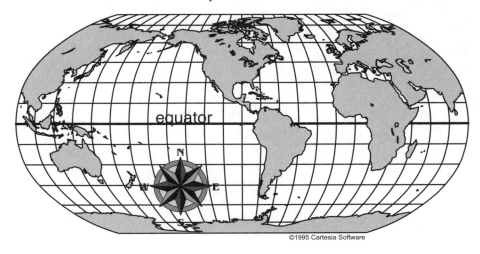

©1995 Cartesia Software

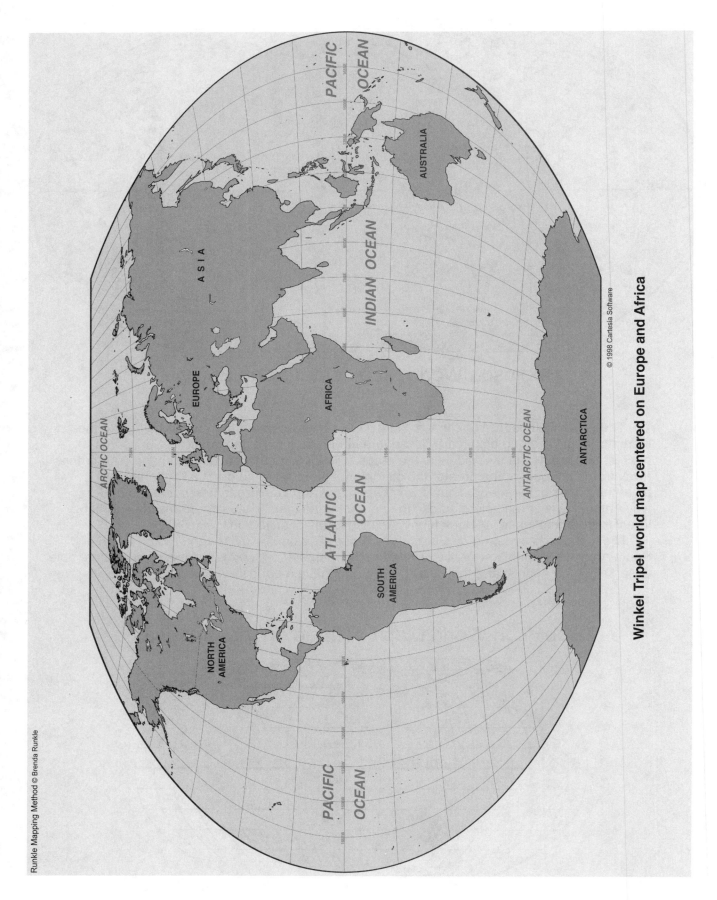

© 1998 Cartesia Software

**Winkel Tripel world map centered on Europe and Africa**

Runkle Mapping Method © Brenda Runkle

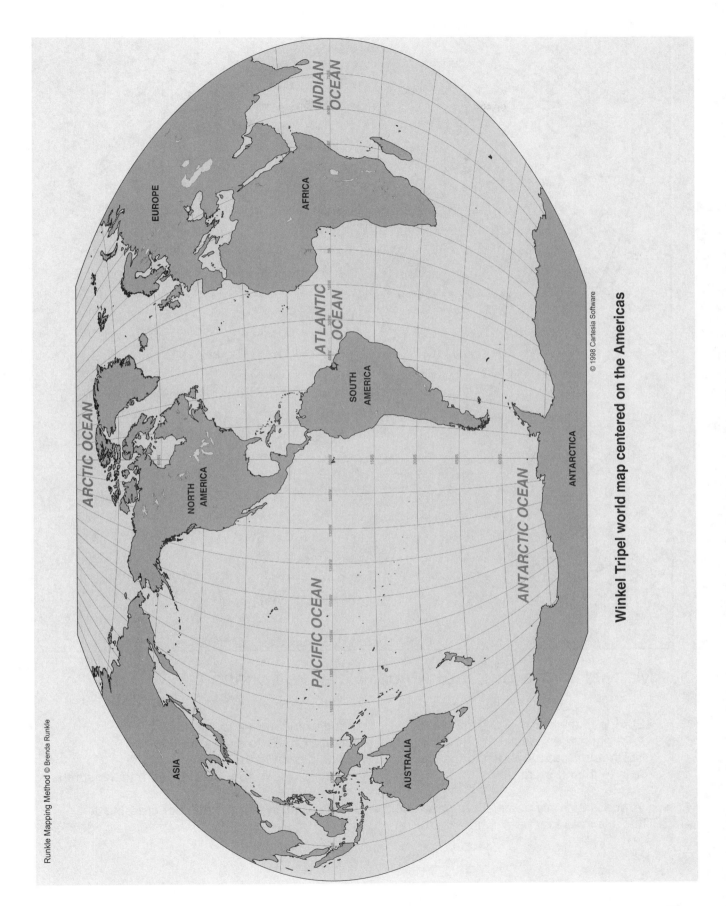

© 1998 Cartesia Software

**Winkel Tripel world map centered on the Americas**

Runkle Mapping Method - Africa ©Brenda Runkle

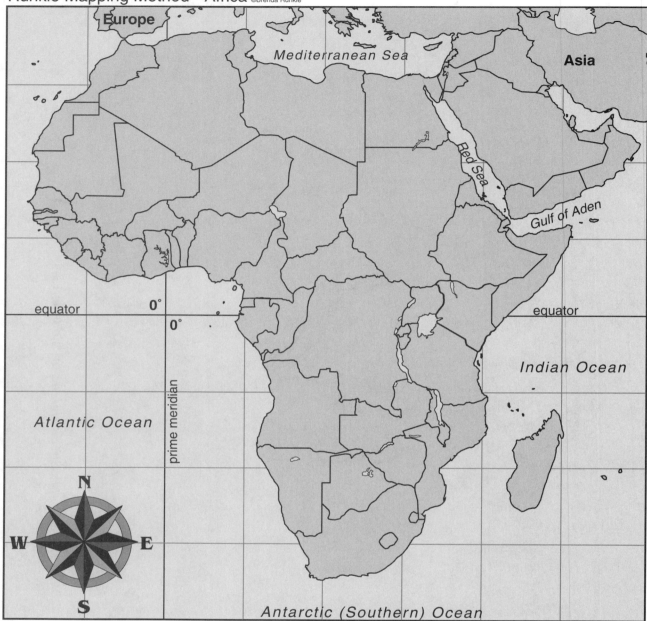

# Map #1 In the Study of Africa: Relative Location

- Europe to the north.
- Antarctica to the south.
- North and South America to the west.
- Asia to the northeast.

- Mediterranean Sea to the north.
- Atlantic Ocean to the west.
- Indian Ocean to the east.
- Antarctic Ocean (Southern Ocean) to the south.

Africa is the only continent to have both the prime meridian and the equator crossing it. Thus it is in all four hemispheres.

Runkle Mapping Method - Africa ©Brenda Runkle

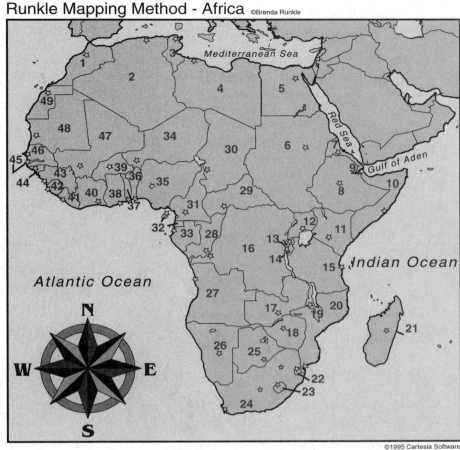

©1995 Cartesia Software

# Map #4 in the Study of Africa: The 49 Capitals

1. Rabat, Morocco
2. Algiers, Algeria
3. Tunis, Tunisia
4. Tripoli, Libya
5. Cairo, Egypt
6. Khartoum, Sudan
7. Asmara, Eritrea
8. Addis Ababa, Ethiopia
9. Djibouti City, Djibouti
10. Mogadishu, Somalia
11. Nairobi, Kenya
12. Kampala, Uganda
13. Kigali, Rwanda
14. Bujumbura, Burundi
15. Dar-es-Salaam, Tanzania
16. Kinshasa, Zaire (Democratic Republic of the Congo)
17. Lusaka, Zambia
18. Harare, Zimbabwe
19. Lilongwe, Malawi
20. Maputo, Mozambique

21. Antananarivo, Madagascar
22. Mbabane, Swaziland
23. Maseru, Lesotho
24. Cape Town (legislative), Bloemfontein (judicial), Pretoria (executive), South Africa
25. Gaborone, Botswana
26. Windhoek, Namibia
27. Luanda, Angola
28. Brazzaville, Republic of the Congo
29. Bangui, Central African Republic
30. N'Djamena, Chad
31. Yaounde, Cameroon
32. Malabo, Equatorial Guinea
33. Libreville, Gabon
34. Niamey, Niger
35. Abuja, Nigeria
36. Porto Novo, Benin

37. Lomé, Togo
38. Accra, Ghana
39. Ouagadougou, Burkina Faso
40. Yamoussoukro, Ivory Coast
41. Monrovia, Liberia
42. Freetown, Sierra Leone
43. Conakry, Guinea
44. Bissau, Guinea-Bissau
45. Banjul, The Gambia
46. Dakar, Senegal
47. Bamako, Mali
48. Nouakchott, Mauritania
49. Laayoune, Western Sahara

17

Runkle Mapping Method - Africa ©Brenda Runkle

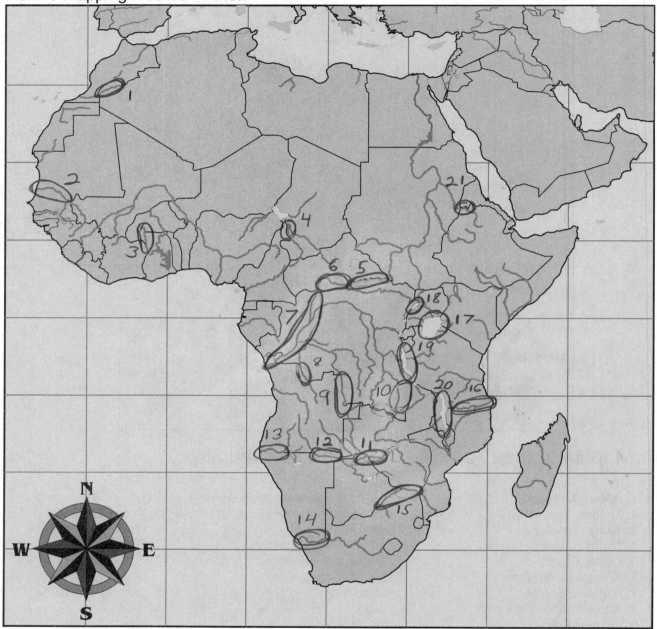

©1995 Cartesia Software

# Map #5 in the Study of Africa: Enrichment Activity

Use this map of Africa to determine where a river forms a boundary between countries, please. This is a critical thinking skill activity to help you develop your powers of observation. It is important to be aware of physical features that form boundaries. Called natural boundaries, they will play an important role throughout history as they affect the movement of people, goods and ideas. Natural boundaries will be visible to the eye, form a barrier of some sort and be easily recognized. Thus, they make good national and international boundaries. Use map #6 to check for accuracy and to find the names of rivers forming boundaries.

Hint: Refer back to map #1 to check political boundaries of countries.

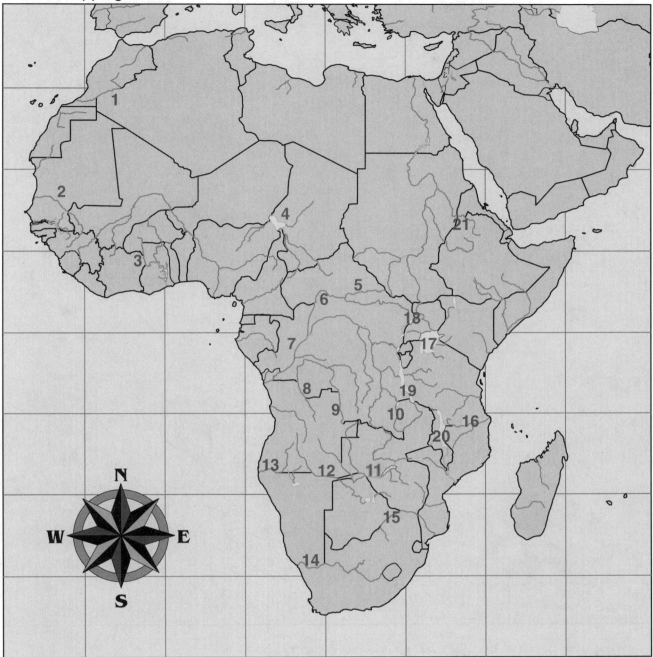

©1995 Cartesia Software

# Map #6 in the Study of Africa: Boundary Rivers

1. Oued Draa
2. Senegal River
3. Black Volta
4. Lake Chad
5. Mbomou
6. Ubangi

7. Congo
8. Kwango
9. Kasai
10. Luvua
11. Zambezi

12. Kwando
13. Kunene
14. Orange
15. Limpopo
16. Ruvuma

17. Lake Victoria
18. Lake Albert
19. Lake Tanganyika
20. Lake Nyasa
21. Tekeze

3/25/08

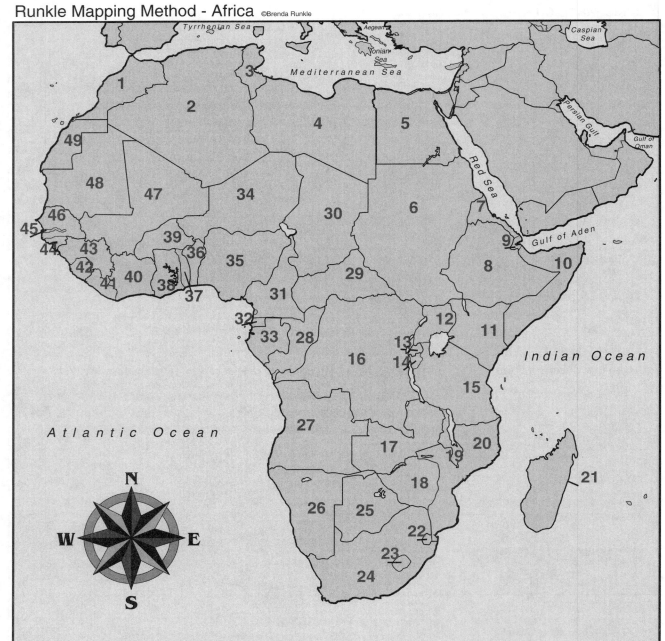

©1995 Cartesia Software

# Map #7 in the Study of Africa: Map Test

On a clean sheet of paper, list the numbers 1-49. Write the name of each country beside each corresponding number. Next to the name of the country, write the name of the capital. Be sure to check your spelling. One of the marks of a well educated person is correct spelling. For each name you misspell, please write it ten times correctly, or until you are confident that you have mastered the correct spelling.

# Learning Africa the Easy Way!

Learning the 49 countries of Africa is not a hard task when you look for patterns in their names and sounds. Memorization is easiest when you learn in groups of odd numbers such as 5, 7, and 9. Never attempt to learn more than 9 at one time. For some reason, retention drops off when you attempt more than 9. We want to say each country at least five times in order daily, write them and check for spelling. Don't take any shortcuts! Read the name, say it out loud, write it and check for spelling. Regardless of your learning style, if you follow this pattern you will master all the countries of the world with ease!

### Morocco, Algeria, Tunisia, Libya, Egypt

Let's begin with northern Africa. Morocco, Algeria, Tunisia, Libya, Egypt. Five countries all with coasts along the Mediterranean Sea. All but one share a common southern border. Can you close your eyes and find the country that does not share a common southern border? It is Tunisia, located between Algeria and Libya. Now look at the map, point to each country in order, and name them five times. Close your eyes and try to see them in your mind. Mental mapping is a skill we will develop over this course of study. You will be able to find any place in the world without requiring a prompt of any type.

### Sudan, Eritrea, Ethiopia, Djibouti, Somalia

The next countries will be Sudan, Eritrea, Ethiopia, Djibouti and Somalia. Again, five countries. Four have a common boundary, the Red Sea. Which country does not have access to the Red Sea? Ethiopia. Eritrea used to belong to Ethiopia, but in 1993 declared its independence. Look at the odd spelling of Djibouti. We do not have any words in the English language that combine *d* and *j*. Somalia lies on the "horn" of Africa. If you turn your map of Africa to the left, it looks like a horse or lizard of some sort with a horn!

### Kenya, Uganda, Rwanda, Burundi, Tanzania

The next five are Kenya, Uganda, Rwanda, Burundi, and Tanzania. We do not have the letter combination *rw* in our language. A fun way to remember the middle three countries is to give them an identity. I always told my students to think of them together as that ugly Uganda Rwanda Burundi who ate all their cookies. So the three countries became the name of an imaginary person, Uganda Rwanda Burundi. I chose the word ugly simply because I could not think of another word beginning with *ug*. If you can come up with a better suggestion, please let me know!

### Zaire, Zambia, Zimbabwe

Now begin the *Z* names. We do not have many words that use the letter *z*, so it is really fun to let the *z* sound resonate in your nose and kind of buzz around. Notice Tanzania. Now add Zaire, Zambia and Zimbabwe. Zaire has changed its name to The Democratic Republic of the Congo. But we will call it Zaire for the time being, at least until it stabilizes. The little country of Congo on the west coast of Africa is now the Congo Republic.

### Malawi, Mozambique, Madagascar

Now we group the *M* countries together. They are *M*alawi, *M*ozambique and *M*adagascar. See how easy it is to set up patterns that make it easier to learn!

3/25/08

## Swaziland, Lesotho, South Africa, Botswana, Namibia, Angola

The next six countries are Swaziland, Lesotho, South Africa, Botswana, Namibia and Angola. Swaziland and Lesotho are tribal homelands or kingdoms much like our Indian reservations. They are very poor and most of the people go into South Africa to work. Namibia has a desert that goes right down to the ocean. Parts of the Namib Desert receive little if any rain. Animals survive by licking the morning dew off any available surface such as a rock, a leaf or even their own backs.

## Congo Republic, Central African Republic, Chad, Cameroon

The next four countries all begin with *C*: *C*ongo Republic, *C*entral African Republic, *C*had, and *C*ameroon.

## Equatorial Guinea, Gabon,

The little country right above the equator is Equatorial Guinea, with Gabon to the south. Although it is named *Equatorial* Guinea, its absolute location is  2°N. That means it lies 2° north of the equator. Look closely and notice the small country caught between the Congo Republic and Zaire. That is Cabinda and belongs to Angola. I don't count it as one of the 49 countries because it is not an independent nation.

## Niger, Nigeria, Benin, Togo, Ghana

The next five are Niger and Nigeria, linked with Benin, Togo and Ghana.

## Burkina Faso

Burkina Faso sits on top of Benin, Togo and Ghana. It used to be called Upper Volta and its major river is still called the Volta.

## Ivory Coast, Liberia, Sierra Leone, Guinea, Guinea-Bissau

The next five countries are the Ivory Coast, Liberia, Sierra Leone, Guinea and Guinea-Bissau. In some almanacs the Ivory Coast is listed by its French name, Cote d'Ivoire. In fact, French is the official language and France is its strongest trading partner. Liberia was founded by freed slaves from America in 1822. However, today it is a country full of unrest and civil war. All five of these countries have coastlines along the Atlantic.

## The Gambia, Senegal, Mali, Mauritania, Western Sahara

Our last five countries are The Gambia, which is completely surrounded by Senegal, then Mali, Mauritania and Western Sahara.

There are only 13 land-locked countries on the continent of Africa. Look at your map and find them, please. Isn't it amazing that 36 of the 49 countries touch an ocean or sea?

The key to long-term retention is to practice every day. In fact, when you are watching the news or reading a book and a country is mentioned, close your eyes and find it on your mental map. Always use your knowledge. Never let it lie idle. Keep in mind, when you do not do something for a long time, the strength of the original learning process will determine if you can even do it again. So do not take any shortcuts on this map practice. Never learn a continent and then set it aside for weeks at a time. Mix the continents up and review them daily until you are so good that you can map it all in your mind without help of any kind!

# Pronunciation Guide: The 49 countries of Africa (Map #3)

1. Morocco **mə-rōk´ō**
2. Algeria **ăl-jîr´ē-ə**
3. Tunisia **tōō-nē´zhə**
4. Libya **lĭb´ē-ə**
5. Egypt **ē´jĭpt**
6. Sudan **sōō-dăn´**
7. Eritrea **ĕr´ĭ-trē´ə**
8. Ethiopia **ē´thē-ō´pē-ə**
9. Djibouti **jĭ-bōō´tē**
10. Somalia **sō-mä´lē-ə**
11. Kenya **kĕn´yə**
12. Uganda **yōō-găn´də**
13. Rwanda **rōō-ăn´də**
14. Burundi **bŏŏ-rōōn´dē**
15. Tanzania **tăn´zə-nē´ə**
16. Zaire **zī-îr´**
17. Zambia **zăm´bē-ə**
18. Zimbabwe **zĭm-bäb´wē**
19. Malawi **mə-lä´wē**
20. Mozambique **mō´zəm-bēk´**
21. Madagascar **măd´ə-găs´kər**
22. Swaziland **swä´zē-lănd´**
23. Lesotho **lə-sō´tō**
24. South Africa **south ăf´rĭ-kə**
25. Botswana **bŏt-swä´nə**
26. Namibia **nə-mĭb´ē-ə**
27. Angola **ăng-gō´lə**
28. Congo **kŏng´gō**
29. Central African Republic **sĕn´trəl ăf´rĭ-kən rĭ-pŭb´lĭk**
30. Chad **chăd**
31. Cameroon **kăm ə-rōōn´**
32. Equatorial Guinea **ē´kwə-tôr´ē-əl gĭn´ē**
33. Gabon **gă-bōn´**
34. Niger **nī´jər**
35. Nigeria **nī-jîr´ē-ə**
36. Benin **bə-nĭn´**
37. Togo **tō´gō**
38. Ghana **gä´nə**
39. Burkina Faso **bər-kē´nə fä´sō**
40. Ivory Coast **ī´və-rē kōst**
41. Liberia **lī-bîr´ē-ə**
42. Sierra Leone **sē-ĕr´ə lē-ōn´**
43. Guinea **gĭn´ē**
44. Guinea-Bissau **gĭn´ē bĭ-sou´**
45. Gambia **găm´bē-ə**
46. Senegal **sĕn-ĭ-gôl´**
47. Mali **mä´lē**
48. Mauritania **môr´ĭ-tā´nē-ə**
49. Western Sahara **wĕs´tərn sə-hâr´ə**

| ă pat | oi boy |
|---|---|
| ā pay | ou out |
| âr care | ŏŏ tŏŏk |
| ä father | ōō bōōt |
| ĕ pet | ŭ cut |
| ē be | ûr urge |
| ĭ pit | th thin |
| ī pie | th this |
| îr pier | hw which |
| ŏ pot | zh vision |
| ō toe | ə about |
| ô paw | item |

**Stress marks:**
´ (primary);
´ (secondary), as in
**dictionary (dĭk´shə-nĕr´ē)**

# Pronunciation Guide: The 49 capitals of Africa (Map #4)

1. Rabat  **rə-bät´**
2. Algiers  **ăl-jîrz´**
3. Tunis  **too͞´nĭs**
4. Tripoli  **trĭp´ə-lē**
5. Cairo  **kī´rō**
6. Khartoum  **kär-too͞m´**
7. Asmara  **ăz-mä´rə**
8. Addis Ababa  **ăd´ĭs ăb´ə-bə**
9. Djibouti City  **jĭ-boo͞´tē**
10. Mogadishu  **mŏg´ə-dĭsh´oo͞**
11. Nairobi  **nī-rō´bē**
12. Kampala  **kăm-pä´lə**
13. Kigali  **kĭ-gä´lē**
14. Bujumbura  **boo͞´jəm-boŏr´ə**
15. Dar-es-Salaam  **där´-ĕs-sə-läm´**
16. Kinshasa  **kĭn-shä´sə**
17. Lusaka  **loo͞-sä´kə**
18. Harare  **hə-rär´ā**
19. Lilongwe  **lĭ-lông´wä**
20. Maputo  **mə-poo͞´tō**
21. Antananarivo  **ăn´tə-năn´ə-rē´vō**
22. Mbabane  **əm-bä-bän´**
23. Maseru  **măz´ə-roo͞´**
24. Cape Town  **kāp´toun´**
    Bloemfontein  **bloo͞m´fŏn-tān´**
    Pretoria  **prĭ-tôr´ē-ə**
25. Gaborone  **gä´bə-rōn´**
26. Windhoek  **vĭnt´hoŏk´**
27. Luanda  **loo͞-ăn´də**
28. Brazzaville  **brăz´ə-vĭl´**
29. Bangui  **bäng-gē´**
30. N'Djamena  **ən-jä´mä-nä**
31. Yaounde  **yä-oo͞n-dä´**
32. Malabo  **mə-lä´bō**
33. Libreville  **lē-brə-vēl´**
34. Niamey  **nē-ä´mä**
35. Abuja  **ä-boo͞´jä**
36. Porto-Novo  **pôr´tō-nō´vō**
37. Lomé  **lō-mä´**
38. Accra  **ăk´rə**
39. Ouagadougou  **wä´gə-doo͞´goo͞**
40. Yamoussoukro  **yäm´ə-soo͞´krō**
    Abidjan  **ăb´ĭ-jän´**
41. Monrovia  **mən-rō´vē-ə**
42. Freetown  **frē´toun´**
43. Conakry  **kŏn´ə-krē**
44. Bissau  **bĭ-sou´**
45. Banjul  **bän´joo͞l´**
46. Dakar  **də-kär´**
47. Bamako  **bä´mə-kō´**
48. Nouakchott  **nwäk-shŏt´**
49. Laayoune  **läh-yoo͞n**

| | | |
|---|---|---|
| ă pat | oi boy | |
| ā pay | ou out | |
| âr care | oŏ toŏk | |
| ä father | oo͞ boo͞t | |
| ĕ pet | ŭ cut | |
| ē be | ûr urge | |
| ĭ pit | th thin | |
| ī pie | *th* this | |
| îr pier | hw which | |
| ŏ pot | zh vision | |
| ō toe | ə about | |
| ô paw | item | |

**Stress marks:**
´ (primary);
´ (secondary), as in
**dictionary (dĭk´shə-nĕr´ē)**

# Pronunciation Guide: Boundary Rivers and Lakes of Africa (Map #6)

1. Oued Draa **wäd drä**
2. Senegal **sĕn´ĭ-gôl´**
3. Black Volta **vŏl´tə**
4. Lake Chad **lāk chăd**
5. Mbomou **əm-bō´mōō**
6. Ubangi **yōō-băng´gē**
7. Congo **kŏng´gō**
8. Kwango **kwän´gō**
9. Kasai **kə-sī´**
10. Luvua **lŏŏ´vōō-ə**
11. Zambezi **zăm-bē´zē**
12. Kwando **kwän´dō**
13. Kunene **kōō-nā´nə**
14. Orange **ôr´ĭnj**
15. Limpopo **lĭm-pō´pō**
16. Ruvuma **rŏŏ-vōō´mə**
17. Lake Victoria **lāk vĭk-tôr´ē-ə**
18. Lake Albert **lāk ăl´bərt**
19. Lake Tanganyika **lāk tăn´gən-yē´kə**
20. Lake Nyasa **lāk nĭ-ăs´ə**
21. Tekeze **tə-kəz´ə**

| ă pat | oi boy |
|-------|--------|
| ā pay | ou out |
| âr care | ŏŏ tŏŏk |
| ä father | ōō bōōt |
| ĕ pet | ŭ cut |
| ē be | ûr urge |
| ĭ pit | th thin |
| ī pie | *th* this |
| îr pier | hw which |
| ŏ pot | zh vision |
| ō toe | ə about |
| ô paw | item |

**Stress marks:**
´ (primary);
´ (secondary), as in
**dictionary (dĭk´shə-nĕr´ē)**

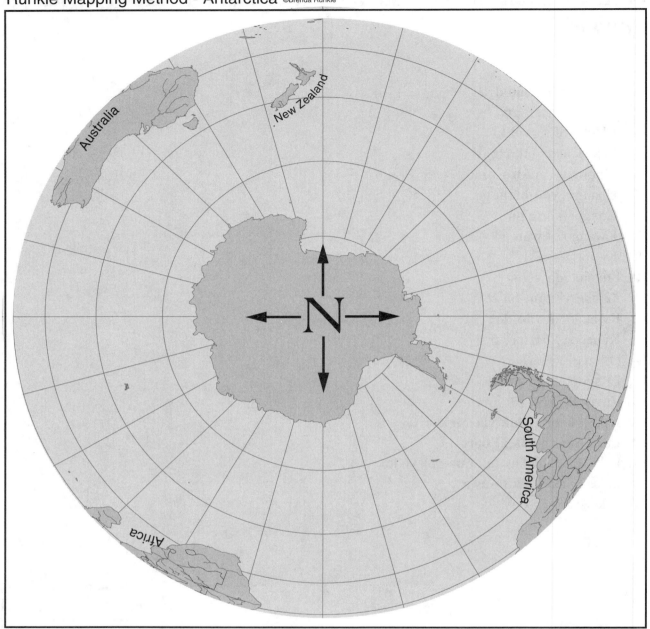

# Map #1 in the Study of Antarctica: Relative Location

• All other continents to the north          • Antarctic ocean on all sides

   Antarctica is the fifth largest continent. It is the highest continent, with an average elevation of 8,000 feet (2,438 m). There are no rivers because the continent is covered with ice. In fact, the average thickness of the ice cap is one mile. There are no permanent human residents in Antarctica. Penguins make up the largest population found on the continent. Estimates range in the millions for the penguin population. If you were standing on the South Pole in Antarctica, any direction you looked would be north. During the winter the sun never rises.

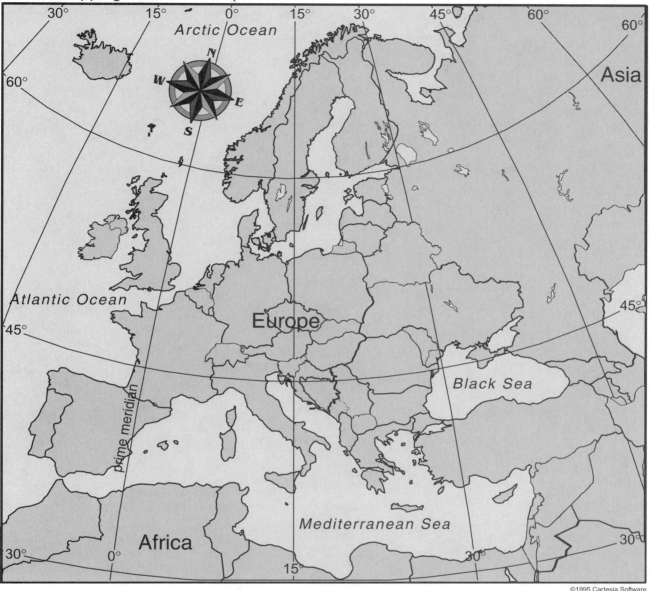

©1995 Cartesia Software

## Map #1 in the Study of Europe: Relative Location

- Africa to the south
- Asia to the east
- North America to the west

- Arctic Ocean to the north
- Atlantic Ocean to the west
- Mediterranean Sea to the south
- Black Sea to the east

Europe is north of the equator, placing it in the Northern Hemisphere. The prime meridian passes through Greenwich, England, placing Europe in the Eastern and Western Hemispheres. The prime meridian is used to establish time.

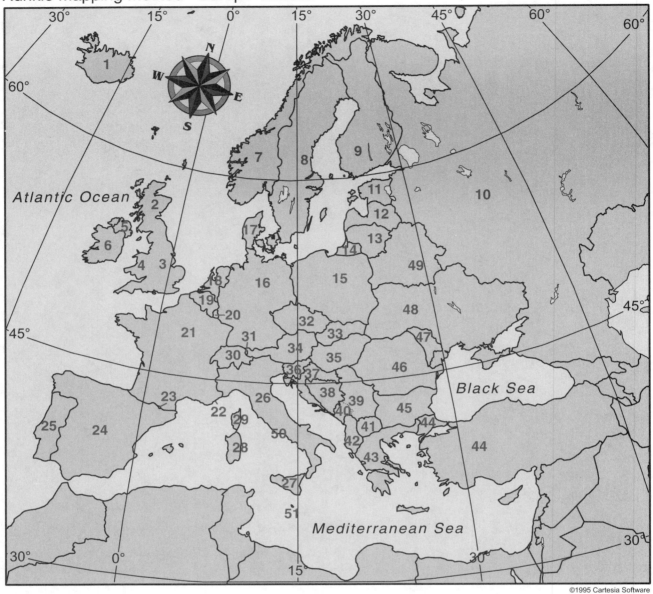

# Map #2 in the Study of Europe: Pretest

Use this map to become familiar with all the countries of Europe. It is always fun to take a test before you begin something new so that you can measure your progress as you learn. Take a pretest and see how many countries of Europe you can name at this point in time. Map #3 will identify the countries.

# Runkle Mapping Method - Europe ©Brenda Runkle

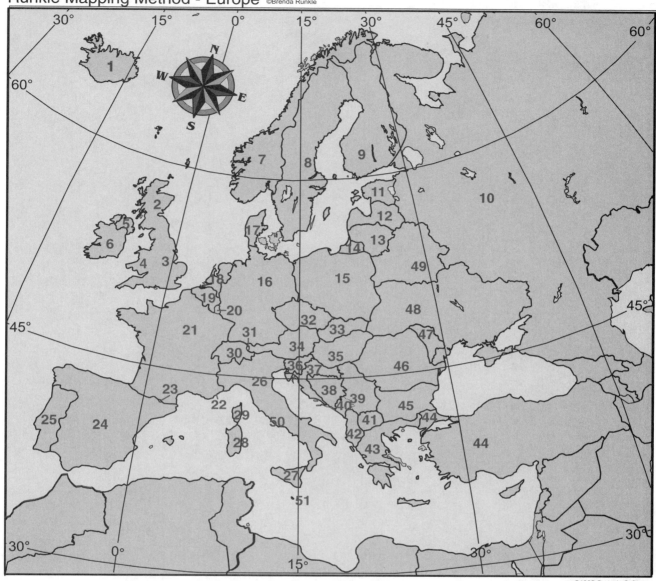

©1995 Cartesia Software

## Map #3 in the Study of Europe: The 51 Countries

1. Iceland
2. Scotland (U.K.)
3. England (U.K.)
4. Wales (U.K.)
5. Northern Ireland (U.K.)
6. Ireland
7. Norway
8. Sweden
9. Finland
10. Russia
11. Estonia
12. Latvia
13. Lithuania

14. Kaliningrad (Russia)
15. Poland
16. Germany
17. Denmark
18. The Netherlands
19. Belgium
20. Luxembourg
21. France
22. Monaco
23. Andorra
24. Spain
25. Portugal
26. Italy

27. Sicily (Italy)
28. Sardinia (Italy)
29. Corsica (France)
30. Switzerland
31. Liechtenstein
32. Czech Republic
33. Slovakia
34. Austria
35. Hungary
36. Slovenia
37. Croatia
38. Bosnia-Herzegovina
39. Serbia

40. Montenegro
    (Yugoslavia)
41. Macedonia
42. Albania
43. Greece
44. Turkey
45. Bulgaria
46. Romania
47. Moldova
48. Ukraine
49. Belarus
50. Vatican City
51. Malta

( ) Indicates country claiming ownership

29

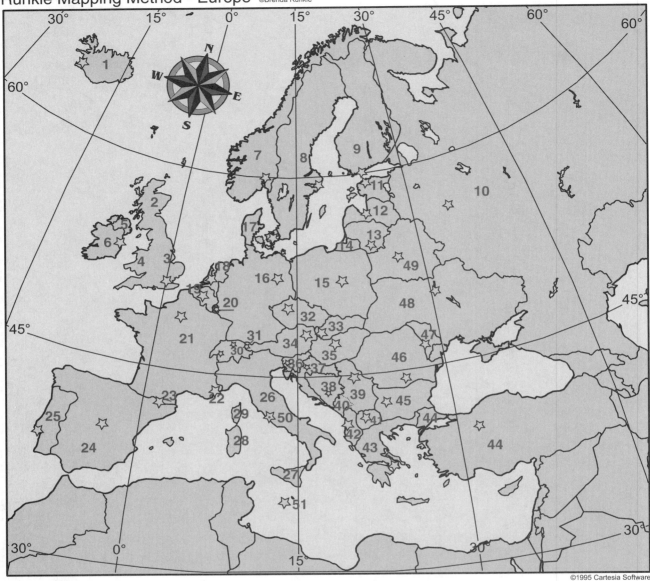

©1995 Cartesia Software

# Map #4 in the Study of Europe: The 51 Capitals

1. Reykjavik, Iceland
2. Edinburgh, Scotland ★
3. London, England ★
4. London, Wales ★
5. Belfast, N. Ireland ★
6. Dublin, Ireland
7. Oslo, Norway
8. Stockholm, Sweden
9. Helsinki, Finland
10. Moscow, Russia
11. Tallinn, Estonia
12. Riga, Latvia
13. Vilnius, Lithuania

★Indicates United Kingdom claiming ownership

14. Moscow, Russia
15. Warsaw, Poland
16. Berlin, Germany
17. Copenhagen, Denmark
18. Amsterdam, The Netherlands
19. Brussels, Belgium
20. Luxembourg, Luxembourg
21. Paris, France
22. Monaco, Monaco
23. Andorra la Vella, Andorra
24. Madrid, Spain
25. Lisbon, Portugal
26. Rome, Italy

27. Rome, Sicily (Italy)
28. Rome, Sardinia (Italy)
29. Paris, Corsica (France)
30. Bern (administrative),
    Lausanne (judicial),
    Switzerland
31. Vaduz, Liechtenstein
32. Prague, Czech Republic
33. Bratislava, Slovakia
34. Vienna, Austria
35. Budapest, Hungary
36. Ljubljana, Slovenia
37. Zagreb, Croatia

38. Sarajevo, Bosnia-
    Herzegovina
39. Belgrade, Serbia
40. Belgrade, Yugoslavia
41. Skopje, Macedonia
42. Tirane, Albania
43. Athens, Greece
44. Ankara, Turkey
45. Sofia, Bulgaria
46. Bucharest, Romania
47. Chisinau, Moldova
48. Kiev, Ukraine
49. Minsk, Belarus
50. Vatican City
51. Valletta, Malta

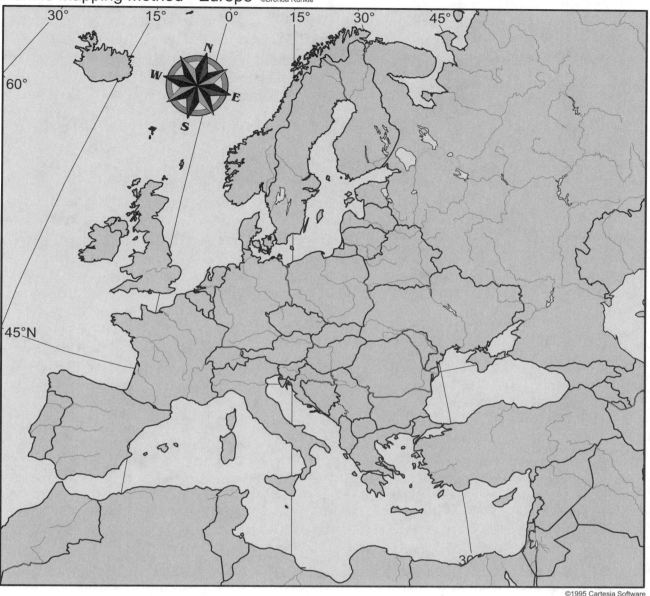

©1995 Cartesia Software

# Map # 5 in the Study of Europe: Enrichment Activity

    Use this map of Europe to determine where a river forms a boundary between countries, please. This is a critical thinking skill activity to help you develop your powers of observation. It is important to be aware of physical features that form boundaries. Called natural boundaries, they will play an important role throughout history as they affect the movement of people, goods and ideas. Natural boundaries will be visible to the eye, form a barrier of some sort and be easily recognized. Thus, they make good national and international boundaries. Use map #6 to check for accuracy and to find the names of rivers forming boundaries.

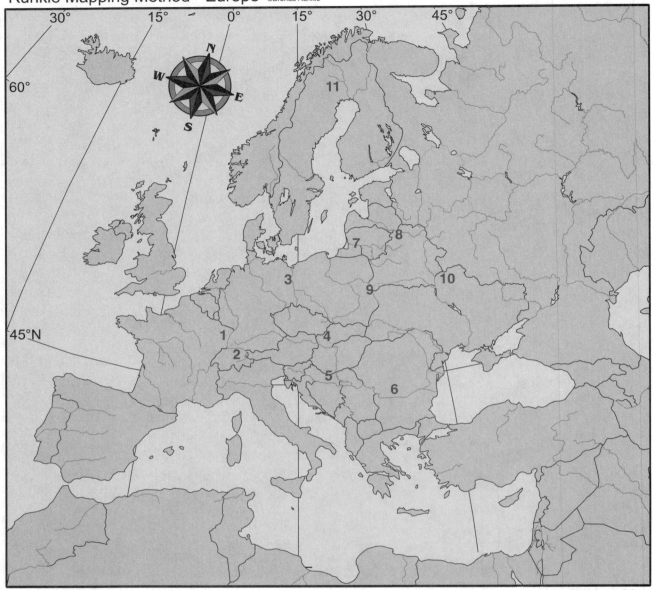

©1995 Cartesia Software

# Map # 6 in the Study of Europe: Boundary Rivers

1. Rhine (France & Germany)
2. Rhine (Switzerland & Germany)
3. Oder
4. Danube (Hungary & Slovakia)
5. Sava
6. Danube (Bulgaria & Romania)
7. Neman
8. Dvina
9. Bug (no kidding!)
10. Sozh
11. Muonioalven

   While you are looking at the map of Europe it is fun to notice there are more rivers flowing to the north than there are rivers flowing to the south! Because the Mississippi is so important to us, we tend to think all rivers flow south, or in our minds from the top of the globe to the bottom. Not so!! Rivers flow from the highest point to the lowest point following the path of least resistance regardless of their location. Thus they can flow in any direction from their highest point!

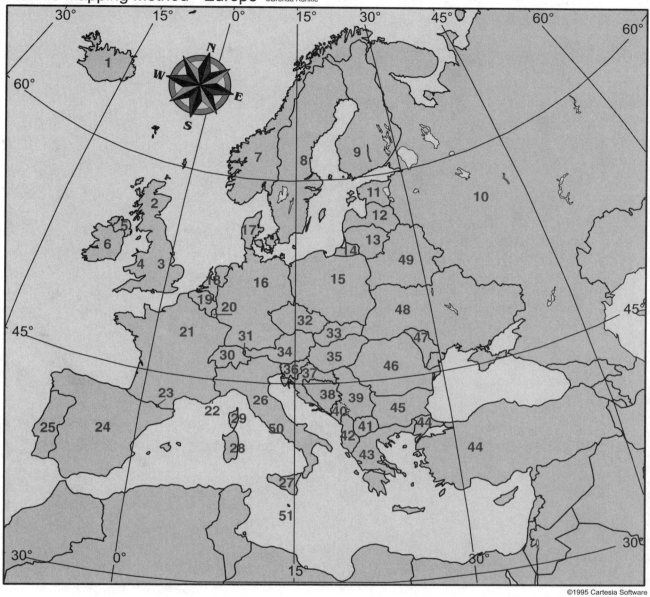

©1995 Cartesia Software

# Map #7 in the Study of Europe: Map Test

On a clean sheet of paper, list the numbers 1-51. Write the name of each country beside each corresponding number. Next to the name of the country, write the name of its capital. Be sure to check your spelling. One of the marks of a well educated person is correct spelling. For each name you misspell, please write it ten times correctly, or until you are confident that you have mastered the correct spelling.

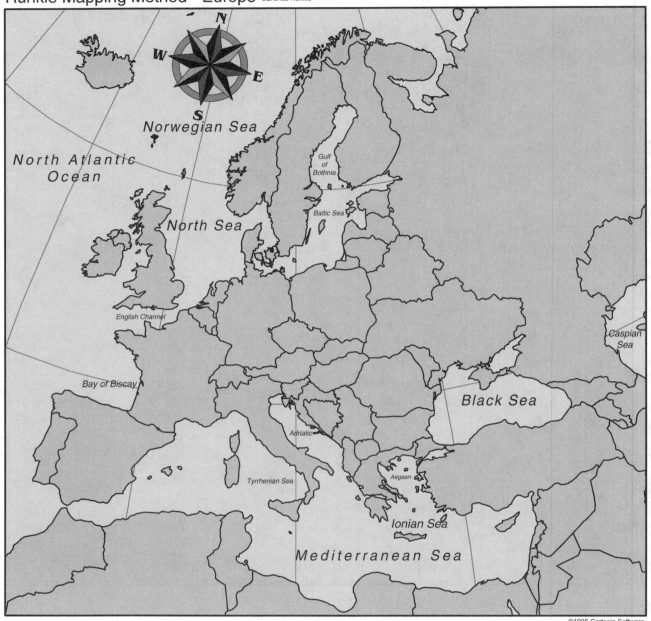

North Atlantic Ocean

Norwegian Sea

Gulf of Bothnia

Baltic Sea

North Sea

English Channel

Caspian Sea

Bay of Biscay

Black Sea

Adriatic

Tyrrhenian Sea

Aegean

Ionian Sea

Mediterranean Sea

©1995 Cartesia Software

# Map # 8 in the Study of Europe: Brain Teasers

Here are some mnemonics used to help memorize countries. See if you can determine which countries are represented by each mnemonic! The first letter of each word will be the first letter of a country. They will all go in order to form a pattern.

**N**ever **S**mell **F**ish
**B**ell's **U**ncle **R**oamed **B**eautiful **G**reek **T**owns
**P**lease **G**o **D**irectly **N**orth **B**efore **L**ily **F**inds **S**pain's **P**orts
**P**eggy **S**ue **F**ound **L**ittle **B**eads **N**ear **D**avid's **G**iant **P**ond
**S**ome **C**urious **B**unnies **H**op **S**everal **M**iles **M**onthly          Good Luck!

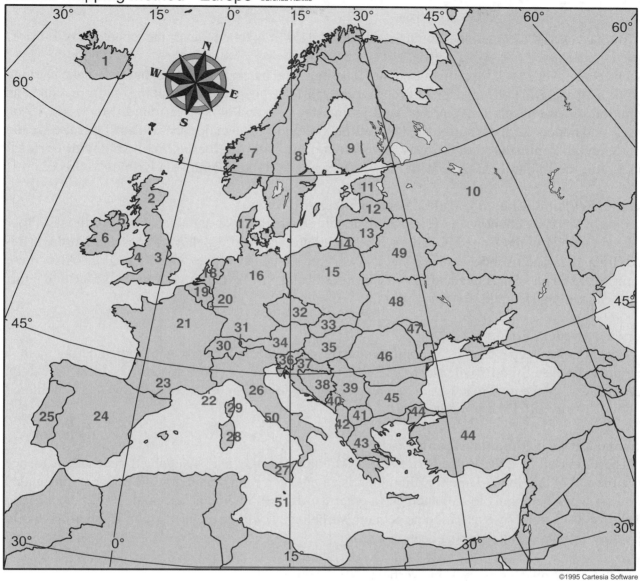

©1995 Cartesia Software

# Map # 9 in the Study of Europe: Europe Fun Map

Mnemonic for Poland, Germany, Denmark, Netherlands, Belgium, Luxembourg, France, Spain, Portugal:
**P**lease **G**o **D**irectly **N**orth **B**efore **L**ily **F**inds **S**pain's **P**ort
or you can go in the opposite direction and say:
**P**eggy **S**ue **F**ound **L**ittle **B**eads **N**ear **D**avid's **G**iant **P**ond

for the former Yugoslavia Slovenia, Croatia, Bosnia-Herzegovina, Serbia, Montenegro, Macedonia:
**S**ome **C**urious **B**unnies **H**op **S**everal **M**iles **M**onthly

for Belarus, Ukraine, Romania, Bulgaria, Greece,Turkey:
**B**ell's **U**ncle **R**oamed **B**eautiful **G**reek **T**owns

for Norway, Sweden and Finland: **N**ever **S**mell **F**ish

# Learning Europe the Easy Way !

We have already learned the  countries of Africa. Now it is time to learn the  countries of Europe.

Once again let's look for patterns, sounds, spellings and natural groupings that will make learning Europe a breeze. Did you notice that Europe is really just one big peninsula sticking out from Asia? The definition of a peninsula is a piece of land jutting out into, and almost surrounded by, a sea. Look closely and notice Europe is surrounded by seas on three sides. The major peninsulas of Europe are the Scandinavian Peninsula with Norway, Sweden and Finland; the Iberian Peninsula with Portugal and Spain; the Italian Peninsula with only Italy; and the Balkan Peninsula with only Greece.

## Iceland, Scotland, England, Wales, Northern Ireland, Ireland

Five of these six countries have *land* in their names, which makes them a natural group. Also, four of the six belong to the United Kingdom. These four are Scotland, England, Wales and Northern Ireland. Ireland gained its independence and is no longer a member of the United Kingdom. Also, these countries are all on islands. Iceland is a volcanic island and only belongs to Europe by virtue of the fact it was claimed by Denmark for many years.

## Norway, Sweden, Finland

I could never keep these three countries straight so I made up a silly way of remembering them, a mnemonic. **N**ever **S**mell **F**ish. Norway, Sweden, Finland. Notice only Norway borders the Arctic Ocean. Russia prevents Finland from having an opening to the Arctic Ocean and Sweden is bordered by both Norway and Finland to the north.

## Estonia, Latvia, Lithuania, Kaliningrad

These four all face the Baltic Sea. Estonia, Latvia and Lithuania have gained their independence since the fall of the Soviet Union. Kaliningrad is an *oblast*, a funny name for one country surrounded by others while belonging to still another. In other words, Kaliningrad is surrounded by Lithuania and Poland yet is claimed by Russia. Some economists believe it will be the next Hong Kong of the world with duty-free shopping, banking centers, etc.

## Poland, Germany, Denmark, The Netherlands, Belgium

All of these five countries have sea coasts. Germany is now one united country. After WWII it was divided into East Germany  and West Germany. West Germany was controlled by the Allies and developed a free-enterprise economy, while East Germany fell behind the Iron Curtain of communism and remained poor, underdeveloped and polluted.

## Luxembourg, France, Monaco, Andorra, Spain and Portugal

Country #20 on the map is the tiny country of Luxembourg and 23 is the tiny country of Andorra, nestled in the Pyrennes. Monaco, number 22,  is only 0.75 square miles in size yet home to the rich and famous. This independent principality has been ruled by Prince Rainier's family for over 300 years. His late wife was the former Grace Kelly, an American movie star.

## Italy, Sicily, Sardinia, Corsica, Vatican City and Malta

The way I keep these countries straight is to use the boot shape of Italy to kick Sicily, who hits Sardinia, who then bumps Corsica. Corsica was the birthplace of Napoleon and is still claimed by France. Isn't it interesting that the most famous French emperor wasn't even French! Vatican City is the independent papal state located within Rome, Italy, and Malta is a small island country south of Sicily in the Mediterranean Sea.

## Switzerland, Liechtenstein, Czech Republic, Slovakia, Austria, Hungary

Switzerland is united with Liechtenstein through their monetary unit and postal services. This tiny country is an hereditary monarchy. I remember the pronunciation as "lick ten steins". Notice we jump up to the Czech Republic and Slovakia. These two used to be united, and were called Czechoslovakia until the dissolution of the Soviet Union. The Czechs are more modern and industrialized than the Slovaks, so naturally their standard of living is higher. Austria and Hungary also used to be united into a huge empire.

## Slovenia, Croatia, Bosnia-Herzegovina, Serbia, Montenegro, Macedonia

When the Soviet Union dissolved in 1991, the country of Yugoslavia broke up into six newly independent countries. These countries have diverse cultural, historical, and religious units and are struggling with intense hatreds based on old prejudices and historical events. This is the part of Europe that will probably have some drastic changes as civil wars erupt and boundaries change.

## Albania, Greece, Turkey, Bulgaria

Let's tie these four countries together simply because they are on or adjacent to the Peloponnesus of Greece. Albania was one of the poorest communist nations. Greece is fiercely independent. Turkey is a member of NATO and one of our allies. It will be interesting to watch what happens with that relationship as the Turks dam the Tigris and Euphrates Rivers and continue to persecute the Kurds. Turkey plans on controlling the waters of the Tigris and Euphrates to provide hydroelectric power for industry, agriculture and increased political influence. The plans are to sell water to Syria and Israel, as well as Iran and Iraq. Watch the news and see what happens here.

## Romania, Moldova, Ukraine, Byelarus (Belarus)

The Ukraine is the breadbasket of Russia and has very rich soil. Look at the Ukraine on your map and notice it extends from the west to the east at the same latitude. When the crops ripen they ripen at the same time. The North American Great Plains, our breadbasket, extend from the south to the north. This means the same wheat combines that begin the harvest in Texas can cut wheat all the way to Canada. Unfortunately, wheat in the Ukraine and Byelarus ripens at the same time because it is all at the same latitude. The communist government centralized all the farm machinery and everyone has to share the very limited number of machines. Well, who gets their crops harvested first and whose crops are left to rot in the fields? This obviously leads to poor crop yield and hunger.

# Pronunciation Guide: The 51 countries of Europe (Map #3)

1. Iceland  ĭs′lənd
2. Scotland  skŏt′lənd
3. England  ĭng′lənd
4. Wales  wāls
5. Northern Ireland  nôr′thərn ĭr′lənd
6. Ireland  ĭr′lənd
7. Norway  nôr′wā
8. Sweden  swē′dən
9. Finland  fĭn′lənd
10. Russia  rŭsh′ə
11. Estonia  ĕs-tōn′ē-ə
12. Latvia  lăt′vē-ə
13. Lithuania  lĭth′ōō-ā′nē-ə
14. Kaliningrad  kə-lē′nĭn-grăd
15. Poland  pō′lənd
16. Germany  jûr′mə-nē
17. Denmark  dĕn′märk
18. The Netherlands  thə nĕth′ər-ləndz
19. Belgium  bĕl′jəm
20. Luxembourg  lŭk′səm-bûrg′
21. France  frăns
22. Monaco  mŏn′ə-kō
23. Andorra  ăn-dôr′ə
24. Spain  spān
25. Portugal  pôr′chə-gəl
26. Italy  ĭt′l-ē
27. Sicily  sĭs′ə-lē′
28. Sardinia  sär-dĭn′ē-ə
29. Corsica  kôr′sĭ-kə
30. Switzerland  swĭt′sər-lənd
31. Liechtenstein  lĭk′tən-stīn′
32. Czech Republic  chĕk rĭ-pŭb′lĭk
33. Slovakia  slō-vä′kē-ə
34. Austria  ô′strē-ə
35. Hungary  hŭng′gə-rē
36. Slovenia  slō-vē′nē-ə
37. Croatia  krō-ā′shə
38. Bosnia-Herzegovina  bŏz′nē-ə-hĕrt′sə-gō-vē′nə
39. Serbia  sûr′bē-ə
40. Montenegro  mŏn′tə-nē′grō
41. Macedonia  măs′ĭ-dōn′ē-ə
42. Albania  ăl-bā′nē-ə
43. Greece  grēs
44. Turkey  tûr′kē
45. Bulgaria  bŭl-gâr′ē-ə
46. Romania  rō-mā′nē-ə
47. Moldova  mŏl-dō′və
48. Ukraine  yōō-krān′
49. Belarus  bĕl′ə-rōōs′
50. Vatican City  văt′ĭ-kən sĭt′ē
51. Malta  môl′tə

| | |
|---|---|
| ă pat | oi boy |
| ā pay | ou out |
| âr care | ŏŏ took |
| ä father | ōō boot |
| ĕ pet | ŭ cut |
| ē be | ûr urge |
| ĭ pit | th thin |
| ī pie | th this |
| îr pier | hw which |
| ŏ pot | zh vision |
| ō toe | ə about |
| ô paw | item |

**Stress marks:**
′ (primary);
′ (secondary), as in
**dictionary (dĭk′shə-nĕr′ē)**

# Pronunciation Guide: The 51 capitals of Europe (Map #4)

1. Reykjavik  **rā´kyə-vēk´**
2. Edinburgh  **ĕd´n-bûr´ə**
3. London  **lŭn´dən**
4. London  **lŭn´dən**
5. Belfast  **bĕl´făst**
6. Dublin  **dŭb´lĭn**
7. Oslo  **ŏz´lō**
8. Stockholm  **stŏk´hōm**
9. Helsinki  **hĕl-sĭng´kē**
10. Moscow  **mŏs´kō**
11. Tallin  **tăl´ĭn**
12. Riga  **rē´gə**
13. Vilnius  **vĭl´nē-əs**
14. Moscow  **mŏs´kō**
15. Warsaw  **wôr´sô**
16. Berlin  **bər-lĭn´**
17. Copenhagen  **kō´pən-hā´gən**
18. Amsterdam  **am´stər-dăm´**
19. Brussels  **brŭs´əls**
20. Luxembourg  **lŭk´səm-bûrg´**
21. Paris  **păr´ĭs**
22. Monaco  **mŏn´ə-kō**
23. Andorra la Vella  **ăn-dôr´ə lə vĕl-ə**
24. Madrid  **mə-drĭd´**
25. Lisbon  **lĭz´bən**
26. Rome  **rōm**
27. Rome  **rōm**
28. Rome  **rōm**
29. Paris  **păr´ĭs**
30. Bern  **bûrn**
    Lausanne  **lō-zăn´**
31. Vaduz  **vä-dōōts´**
32. Prague  **präg**
33. Bratislava  **brăt´ĭ-slä´və**
34. Vienna  **vē-ĕ´nə**
35. Budapest  **bōō´də-pĕst**
36. Ljubijana  **lōō´blē-ä´nə**
37. Zagreb  **zä´grĕb**
38. Sarajevo  **săr´ə-yā´vō**
39. Belgrade  **bĕl´grād**
40. Belgrade  **bĕl´grād**
41. Skopje  **skôp´yā´**
42. Tirane  **tə-rä´nə**
43. Athens  **ăth´ĭnz**
44. Ankara  **ăng´kər-ə**
45. Sofia  **sō´fē-ə**
46. Bucharest  **bōō´kə-rĕst´**
47. Chisinau  **kē´shē-nŭ´ōō**
48. Kiev  **kē´ĕf**
49. Minsk  **mĭnsk**
50. Vatican City  **văt´ĭ-kən sĭt´ē**
51. Valletta  **və-lĕt-ə**

| | | |
|---|---|---|
| ă pat | oi boy | |
| ā pay | ou out | |
| âr care | ŏŏ tŏŏk | |
| ä father | ōō bōōt | |
| ĕ pet | ŭ cut | |
| ē be | ûr urge | |
| ĭ pit | th thin | |
| ī pie | *th* this | |
| îr pier | hw which | |
| ŏ pot | zh vision | |
| ō toe | ə about | |
| ô paw | item | |

**Stress marks:**
´ (primary);
´ (secondary), as in
**dictionary (dĭk´shə-nĕr´ē)**

# Pronunciation Guide: Boundary Rivers of Europe (Map #6)

1. Rhine  **rīn**
2. Rhine  **rīn**
3. Oder  **ō´dər**
4. Danube  **dăn´yo͞ob**
5. Sava  **sä´və**
6. Danube  **dăn´yo͞ob**
7. Neman  **nĕm´ən**
8. Dvina  **dvē-nä**
9. Bug  **bo͞og**
10. Sozh  **sôsh**
11. Muonio  **mwô-nē´ō**

| ă | pat | oi | boy |
|---|---|---|---|
| ā | pay | ou | out |
| âr | care | o͝o | to͝ok |
| ä | father | o͞o | bo͞ot |
| ĕ | pet | ŭ | cut |
| ē | be | ûr | urge |
| ĭ | pit | th | thin |
| ī | pie | *th* | this |
| îr | pier | hw | which |
| ŏ | pot | zh | vision |
| ō | toe | ə | about |
| ô | paw | | item |

**Stress marks:**
´ (primary);
´ (secondary), as in
**dictionary (dĭk´shə-nĕr´ē)**

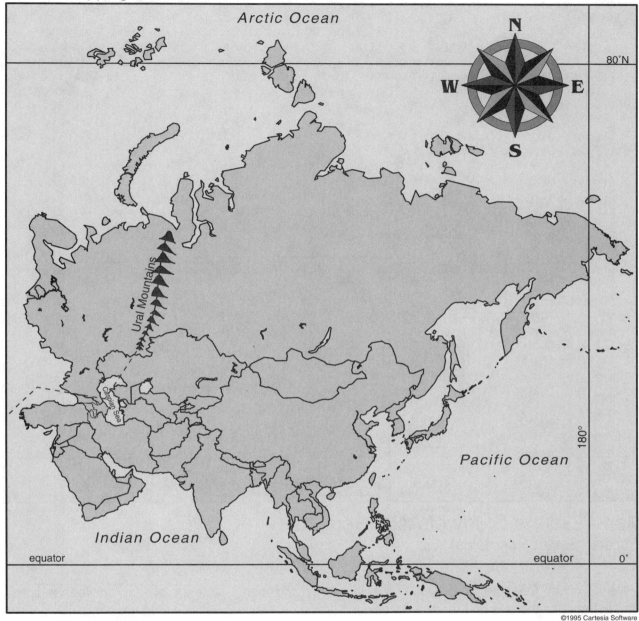

©1995 Cartesia Software

# Map #1 in the Study of Asia: Relative Location

- Europe and Africa to the west.
- Australia to the southeast.
- North and South America to the east.

- Arctic Ocean to the north.
- Pacific Ocean to the east.
- Indian Ocean to the south.

Notice the Ural Mountains, the point at which Europe and Asia joined. Follow the dotted line down to the Caspian Sea, then across Georgia and Armenia and you will see the whole seam. The Urals are the physical boundary between Europe and Asia. Physical Asia is all the land east of the Urals. Political Asia includes the part of Russia west of the Urals. Look closely and notice that Asia is in all four hemispheres, with land north and south of the equator as well as east and west of 180°. Russia is the largest country in the world and China is third largest.

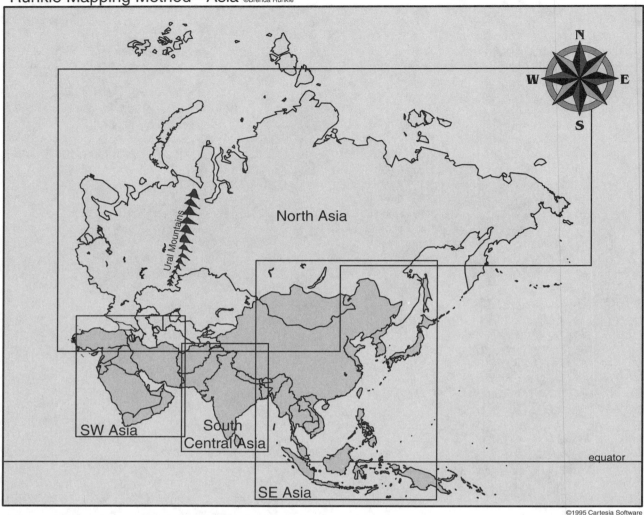

North Asia

Ural Mountains

SE Asia

SW Asia

South Central Asia

equator

©1995 Cartesia Software

# Map #2 in the Study of Asia: Regions
(Former Soviet Republics)

We will divide Asia into four regions for ease of memorization. Notice the overlap between regions. That is because there is no firm rule concerning which countries must lie within each region. These groupings are based upon physical and cultural similarities. By overlapping we form connections that help to place countries in their correct relative locations as well. In order to see the "big picture", please refer to this map as you study each region.

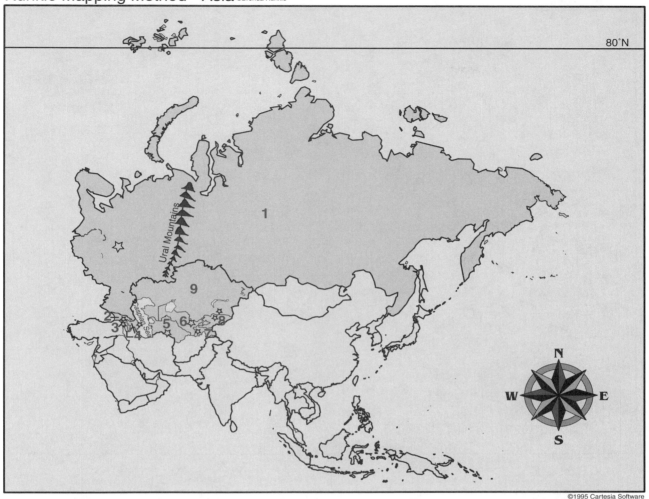

80°N

©1995 Cartesia Software

# Map #3 in the Study of Asia: Former Soviet Republics and Capitals

1. Moscow, Russia
2. Tbilisi, Georgia
3. Yerevan, Armenia

4. Baku, Azerbaijan
5. Ashgabat, Turkmenistan
6. Tashkent, Uzbekistan

7. Dushanbe, Tajikistan
8. Bishkek, Kyrgyzstan
9. Almaty, Kazakhstan

It is important to place these countries in their correct relative location for ease of memorization. Only one country, Russia, forms the northern border. Important bodies of water are the Caspian Sea and Aral Sea. The small body of water just to the east of the Caspian Sea is the Sea of Azov. The five "stans" are landlocked, remote, and almost inaccessible.

Armenia, Georgia, and Azerbaijan are in the Caucasus Mountains where there are numerous deadly earthquakes every year. Georgia and Armenia are Christian orthodox countries, while Azerbaijan is Muslim. This has led to tensions and fighting between the newly independent nations. Azerbaijan has more wealth than the others due to oil reserves in the Caspian Sea. The Aral Sea is fast disappearing as Russia diverts water from it to irrigate cotton fields. The fishing industry has been ruined by the increased salinity of the water. This has also become the region with the highest birth defects in the world due to excessive use of fertilizers and insecticides. As the Aral Sea dries up, the climate becomes hotter and drier.

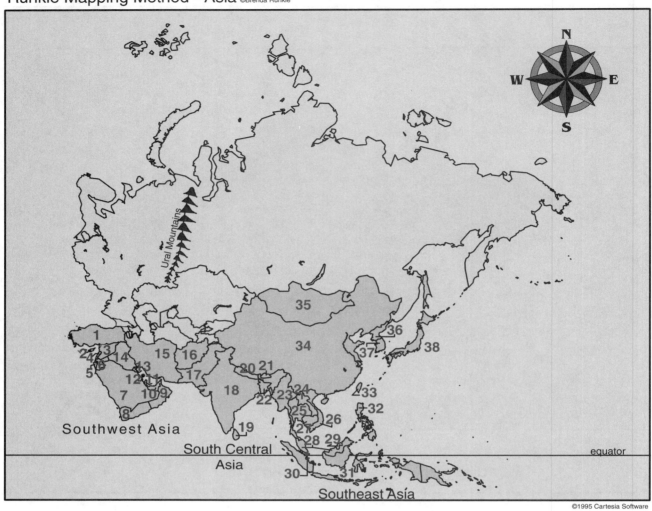

©1995 Cartesia Software

# Map #4 in the Study of Asia: Pretest

We have learned the Commonwealth of Independent States (CIS). Now it is time to look at the rest of the continent. There are 38 countries on this map of Southwest Asia (Middle East), South Central Asia and Southeast Asia. Keep in mind that the Soviet Republics were grouped together and are not included on this map.

Use this map to become familiar with all the countries of Asia. It is always fun to take a test before you begin something new, so that you can measure your progress as you learn. Take a pretest now and see how many countries of Southwest Asia (1-15) you can name. Move on to South Central Asia (16-22) and do the same. Southeast Asia (23-38) will be the last part of the pretest. Map #5 will identify the countries of Southwest Asia. Map #7 will identify the countries of South Central Asia. Map #9 will identify the countries of Southeast Asia.

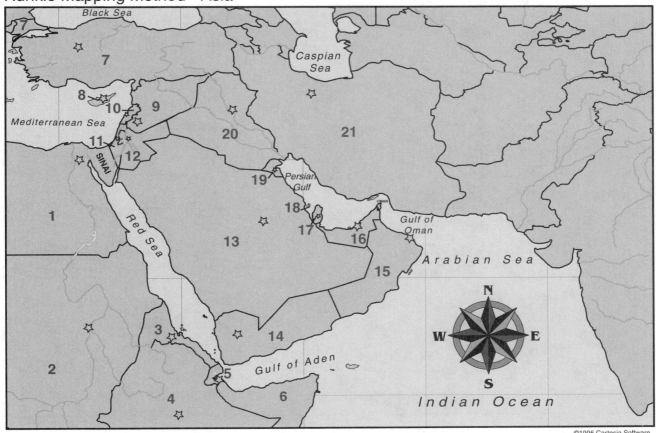

©1995 Cartesia Software

# Map #5 in the Study of Asia: Southwest Asia Countries and Capitals

We will use smaller more detailed maps for each region. Refer to Maps 3 and 4 for the "big picture".

1. Cairo, Egypt
2. Khartoum, Sudan
3. Asmara, Eritrea
4. Addis Ababa, Ethiopia
5. Djibouti City, Djibouti
6. Mogadishu, Somalia
7. Ankara, Turkey

8. Nicosia, Cyprus
9. Damascus, Syria
10. Beirut, Lebanon
11. Jerusalem, Israel
12. Amman, Jordan
13. Riyadh, Saudi Arabia
14. Sanaa, Yemen

15. Muscat, Oman
16. Abu Dhabi, United Arab Emirates
17. Doha, Qatar
18. Manama, Bahrain
19. Kuwait City, Kuwait
20. Baghdad, Iraq
21. Tehran, Iran

Keeping with the incremental pattern of learning, our first six countries belong to a continent we have already learned, Africa. This helps us to place Southwest Asia in its correct relative location east of Africa. Let's begin with Turkey, the only country on two continents. Although the Sinai Peninsula looks as though it should belong to Asia, it is considered part of Africa and is claimed by Egypt. Thus, Turkey is the only country on two continents.

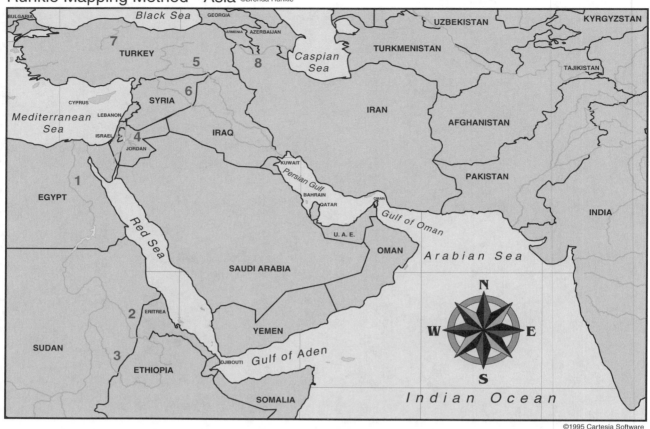

©1995 Cartesia Software

# Map #6 in the Study of Asia: Rivers of Southwest Asia

1. Nile    2. Blue Nile    3. White Nile    4. Jordan    5. Tigris    6. Euphrates    7. Kizil    8. Araks

As we look at this map, remember that water is a valuable and scarce commodity in this region. Notice there are no rivers crossing Saudi Arabia, Yemen, Oman or the United Arab Emirates. Both the Tigris and Euphrates have their headwaters in Turkey. Turkey has built numerous dams along both rivers to provide hydroelectric power, irrigate crops and control the amount of water flowing into Syria and Iraq. The land between these two rivers is known as the Fertile Crescent and is the birthplace of some of the most ancient civilizations.

Let's take a look at the Nile on this map. Almost 95% of all Egyptians live within 12 miles of the river itself. Although the Sahara is dotted with oases, places where underground water rises to the surface, all major cities, industrial centers, and agricultural areas are located in a narrow strip along the Nile.

One way I keep the Tigris and Euphrates straight is by saying the Tigris is on top of the Euphrates.  T for both Tigris and Top. That is why they are numbered the way they are! The Tigris and Euphrates come together at Al Qurnah, Iraq, where they form the Shatt al Arab which becomes the boundary between Iraq and Iran.

The Jordan River rises in Syria and flows approximately 300 miles before emptying into the Dead Sea, which has no outlet. Waters of the Jordan are used for irrigation and hydroelectric power. Only 5 feet deep in most places, it forms a natural boundary between Israel and Jordan and between Israel and Syria.

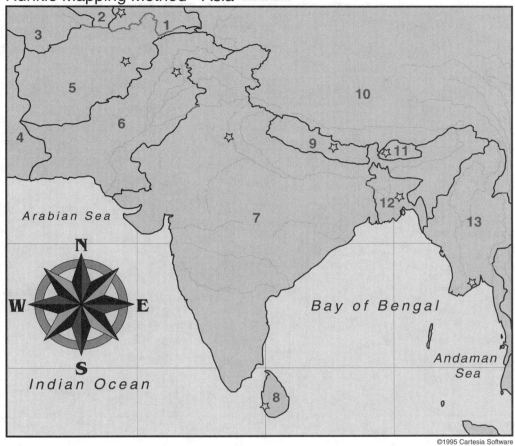

©1995 Cartesia Software

# Map # 7 in the Study of Asia: South Central Asia Countries and Capitals

1. Dushanbe, Tajikistan
2. Tashkent, Uzbekistan
3. Ashgabat, Turkmenistan
4. Tehran, Iran

5. Kabul, Afghanistan
6. Islamabad, Pakistan
7. New Delhi, India
8. Colombo, Sri Lanka

9. Kathmandu, Nepal
10. Beijing, China
11. Thimphu, Bhutan
12. Dhaka, Bangladesh
13. Rangoon, Myanmar

Connecting countries are Turkmenistan, Uzbekistan and Tajikistan to the north and Iran to the west. Notice, Afghanistan and Pakistan also have the root word "stan" but were not included with the other "stans". That is because they have never been a part of the Soviet Union. Russia tried for many years to take over Afghanistan but failed. Many historians feel this war was their "Vietnam" and broke the morale of the Russian people and military. Pakistan and Bangladesh were once part of India. When the British granted independence to India in 1947, they divided the country according to the religious majority of each region. The center part of the country was given to the Hindus, while a new country for the Muslim minority was created to the east and the west. Called East and West Pakistan, the two sections were separated by nearly 1,000 miles, with India in the middle. Although both sections shared the same religion, other problems led to civil war in 1971. West Pakistan became Pakistan and East Pakistan became Bangladesh.

The northern part of Pakistan is mountainous and has K2, the second highest mountain in the world. The southern part has fertile valleys fed by the Indus River. Bangladesh, on the other hand, has the lowest elevation of any country in the world. When the summer monsoons come the entire country floods.

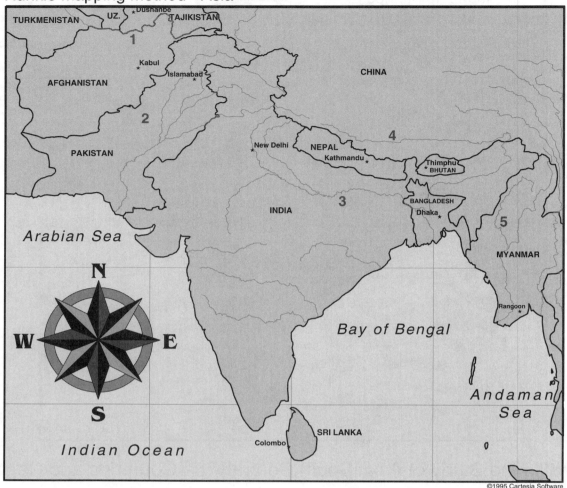

## Map # 8 in the Study of Asia: Rivers of South Central Asia

1. Amu Darya      2. Indus      3. Ganges      4. Brahmaputra      5. Irrawaddy

The Amu Darya is the border between Uzbekistan and Afghanistan and empties into the Aral Sea. The Indus has its headwaters in the Northern Himalayas. So much water is removed for irrigation that only small boats can use the river for transportation.

The Ganges is the sacred river of India. Hindus believe those who die in the Ganges will go to Paradise. Again, so much water is removed for irrigation that it is not navigable for large boats anymore. Its headwaters are in the Himalayas.

The Brahmaputra rises on the northern slopes of the Himalayas. It flows 1,680 miles (2,704 km) before joining with the Ganges to form the Ganges Delta in Bangladesh. It floods annually.

The Irrawaddy, 1,250 miles (2,010 km) long, rises in the north of Myanmar, flows through densely populated areas, and empties into the Bay of Bengal where it forms a rich delta.

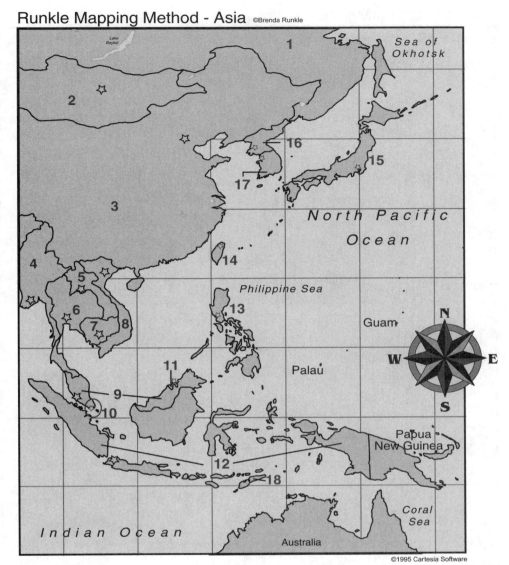

Lake Baykal

Sea of Okhotsk

1

2

16

15

17

3

North Pacific Ocean

14

4

5

Philippine Sea

6

13

Guam

7    8

Palau

11

9

10

12

18

Papua New Guinea

Coral Sea

Indian Ocean

Australia

N  W  E  S

©1995 Cartesia Software

# Map #9 in the Study of Asia: Southeast Asia Countries and Capitals

1. Moscow, Russia
2. Ulan Bator, Mongolia
3. Beijing, China
4. Rangoon, Myanmar (Burma)
5. Vientiane, Laos
6. Bangkok, Thailand

7. Phnom Penh, Cambodia (Kampuchea)
8. Hanoi, Vietnam
9. Kuala Lumpur, Malaysia
10. Singapore, Singapore
11. Bandar Seri Begawan, Brunei
12. Jakarta, Indonesia

13. Manila, Philippines
14. Taipei, Taiwan
15. Tokyo, Japan
16. Pyongyang, North Korea
17. Seoul, South Korea
18. Dili, East Timor

Laos, Cambodia and Vietnam were once ruled by the French and known as French Indochina. Laos, the poorest country in the region, does not have one mile of railroad track and almost no paved roads. Cambodia may well change its name back to Kampuchea. Malaysia lies on the Malay Peninsula and claims part of the island of Borneo. Indonesia is the world's largest archipelago with between 13,000 and 17,000 islands and 210 million people!

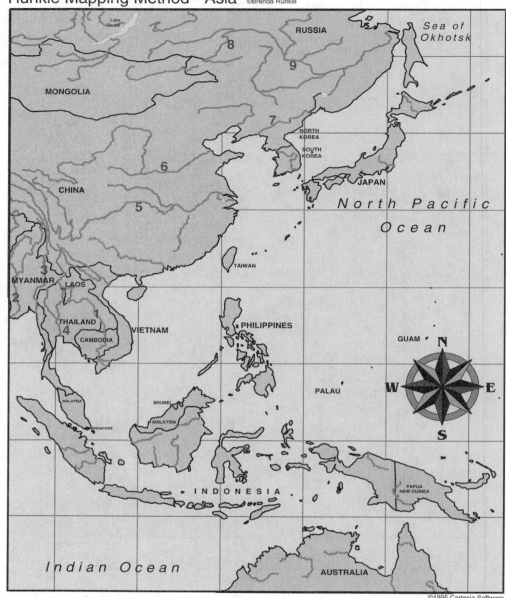

©1995 Cartesia Software

## Map #10 in the Study of Asia: Rivers of Southeast Asia

| | | | | |
|---|---|---|---|---|
| 1. Mekong | 3. Salween | 5. Yangtze | 7. Yalu | 9. Amur |
| 2. Irrawaddy | 4. Chao Phraya | 6. Hwang He | 8. Argun | |

   Perhaps the most important river in the southern region is the Mekong, which serves as a border between Laos/Myanmar and Laos/Thailand. It then flows through Cambodia and forms a huge delta in Vietnam. Myanmar is almost the same size as Texas and has two of Asia's largest rivers, the Irrawaddy and Salween. Thailand has the third largest river in the region, the Chao Phraya, famous for the golden pagodas (temples) lining its shores. The Yangtze and Hwang He are the principal rivers of China. The Yangtze forms the eastern border of Tibet, which no longer exists as an independent country. The Hwang He (Yellow) is "China's sorrow" due to the millions of lives lost in its annual floods. The soil it carries is yellow, hence the name "Yellow". The Yalu River forms the border between China and North Korea. The Argun and Amur form the boundary between Russia and China.

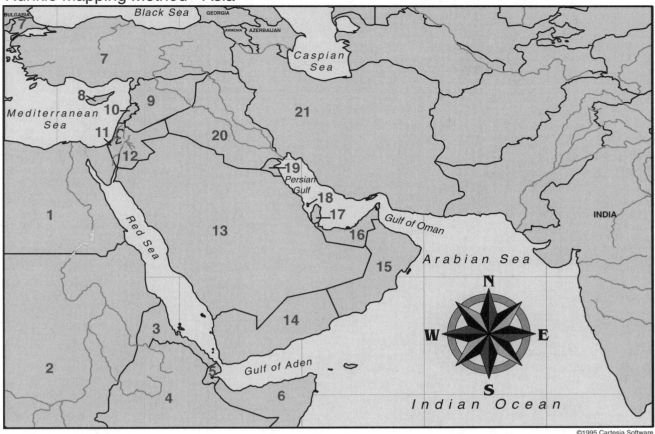

©1995 Cartesia Software

# Map #11 in the Study of Asia: Southwest Asia Map Test

On a clean sheet of paper, list the numbers 1-21. Write the name of each country beside each corresponding number. Next to the name of the country, write the name of its capital. Be sure to check your spelling. One of the marks of a well educated person is correct spelling. For each name you mispell, please write it ten times correctly, or until you are confident that you have mastered the correct spelling.

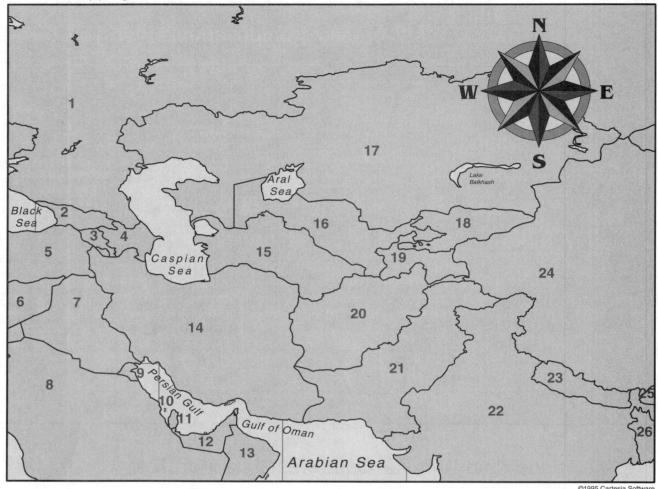

Black Sea

Aral Sea

Caspian Sea

Persian Gulf

Gulf of Oman

Arabian Sea

Lake Balkhash

©1995 Cartesia Software

# Map #12 in the Study of Asia: Central Asia Map Test

On a clean sheet of paper, list the numbers 1-26. Write the name of each country beside each corresponding number. Next to the name of the country, write the name of its capital. Be sure to check your spelling. One of the marks of a well educated person is correct spelling. For each name you misspell, please write it at least ten times correctly, or until you are confident you have mastered the correct spelling.

'1995 Cartesia Software

# Map #13 in the Study of Asia: Southeast Asia Map Test

On a clean sheet of paper, list numbers 1-20. Write the name of each country beside each corresponding number. Next to the name of the country, write the name of its capital. Pay attention now, for there is one number that depends completely on your mental mapping ability. Be sure to check your spelling. One of the marks of a well educated person is correct spelling. For each name you misspell, please write it ten times correctly, or until you are confident that you have mastered the correct spelling.

# Learning Asia the Easy Way!

Let's begin our study of Asia. There are such distinct cultural, historical and physical differences on the world's largest continent that it is necessary to divide it into four separate regions. There is no hard and fast rule about which countries must be in each region, though. And since we use incremental learning, we overlap the regions anyway.

Remember to go over each country at least five times every day. Say them out loud, write them down and listen to someone else say them if possible. Each week be sure to review Africa and Europe as well. You might want to ask critical thinking questions which involve mental mapping skills at this point. For instance, which African countries are closest to Asia? Ask which African and Asian countries border the Mediterranean and Red Seas. Keep asking questions that require observation and thought.

Let me explain a little bit about the importance of the Ural Mountains. They are the point at which the European continent and the Asian continent came together. They are very old and worn down now but are still rich in mineral wealth. East of the Urals is true physical and cultural Asia. West of the Urals is physically Europe but Asian in culture and history. This suture or seam continues down to the Caspian Sea and across the Caucasus Mountains into the Mediterranean. This is a very active earthquake area as the plates still continue to shove against each other.

Always take time to orient yourself as to your relative location. Where is Asia in relation to the United States, the North Pole, Australia, etc.? Mainland Asia lies in three Hemispheres, the Northern, Eastern and Western. It reaches north to 77°45´ N; east to 169°40´ W; south to 1°15´ N; and west to 26°04´ E. Notice the eastern boundary is in the Western Hemisphere and the western boundary is in the Eastern Hemisphere! Also, the southern boundary is in the Northern Hemisphere!

Notice how we have divided Asia into four regions. This division is certainly not written in stone by any means. Please feel free to group them any way you wish. My reasoning followed physical and historical patterns.

Isn't it interesting that one region can have two such different names as the Middle East and Southwestern Asia? It all depends on your perspective, doesn't it? Middle East is the European name for the region and comes from its relative location to the east of Africa and Europe, more or less in the middle of the Eurasian continent. Certainly not an acceptable ethnocentric view as far as the Asians are concerned, is it? Hence, the Asians refer to this same region as Southwestern Asia. It is to the south and west of the rest of the Asian continent!

South Central Asia is just that. It is in the center and to the south of the mass of the Asian continent. Southeast Asia could have been broken down into two additional regions, but the influence of the Pacific Ocean is so great here, it just seemed to make sense to keep them all together.

## Russia, Georgia, Armenia, Azerbaijan, Turkmenistan, Uzbekistan, Tajikistan, Kyrgyzstan, Kazakhstan

These are newly independent countries that almost none of us paid any attention to until the fall of the Soviet Union in 1991. Due to the Russian influence, I grouped them all together. So we will begin with Russia, the largest country in the world. Our nine countries and their capitals are:

| | | | |
|---|---|---|---|
| 1. Russia | Moscow | 6. Uzbekistan | Tashkent |
| 2. Georgia | Tbilisi | 7. Tajikistan | Dushanbe |
| 3. Armenia | Yerevan | 8. Kyrgyzstan | Bishkek |
| 4. Azerbaijan | Baku | 9. Kazakhstan | Almaty |
| 5. Turkmenistan | Ashgabat | | |

Notice five of them have "stan" in their names. This is an ancient word of Altaic or Turkish origin. It is not Russian. It means land or region, so Kazakhstan is the land of the Kazaks! Begin with the first four only and go over them until you can close your eyes and mentally map Russia, Georgia, Armenia, and Azerbaijan without looking at a map. Now add the five "stans," Turkmenistan, Uzbekistan, Tajikistan, Kyrgyzstan and Kazakhstan. Go over them until once again you can see them and their names come to mind easily.

Go over each of these countries at least five times a day. Go in the same order until you can find the countries in your mind. Look at the maps, then close your eyes and find the relative location of each one. For instance, which countries share a border with Russia? Which ones do not? Which countries lie between the Mediterranean Sea and the Caspian Sea? Look at the map and see what other things you can point out. Which countries border China? Which ones border Afghanistan and Pakistan? Which one borders Iran? Which ones border Turkey? The closer you look at each map, the better developed your powers of observation will become.

Learn the countries before you attempt the capitals. It is your decision whether or not to learn every capital. I have never required it for every country. There are, of course, capitals of great importance historically and politically and we should learn them. Watch the news and point out the location of earthquakes, volcanoes, etc. as you study the world. Make learning relevant.

Taking a pretest is always a good idea for several reasons. First of all, it lets you know what you already know at the very beginning of study. It also lets you know if you can skip over a part. But most of all, it becomes very obvious just how much you are learning! We did not have a pretest on the new Commonwealth of Independent States simply because most people have not had a chance to learn them yet. There is never any need for test anxiety on a pretest. It doesn't count for a grade and is for your information only. Over the years I have found pretests actually help reduce test anxiety.

## Turkey, Cyprus, Syria, Lebanon, Israel, Jordan

Now we will learn the countries and capitals of Southwest Asia. Notice on Map #5 we overlap with the bordering countries of Africa. This is all part of the incremental learning pattern and helps to determine relative location. Review the African countries then add the new countries:

| 7. Turkey | Ankara | 10. Lebanon | Beirut |
| 8. Cyprus | Nicosia | 11. Israel | Jerusalem |
| 9. Syria | Damascus | 12. Jordan | Amman |

Stop with these first six countries. Go over them every day until you can find them in your mind's eye and place them in their relative location next to the Mediterranean Sea and Africa.

Turkey is a member of NATO and one of our allies. It controls the entrance and exit to the Black Sea. Once you become aware of the relative location of Russia, you can appreciate the importance of this position. Russia has no warm-water ports except in the Black Sea. Thus, trade and military maneuvers slow down or come to a halt during the frozen winter months. Turkey is our ally. So, if we went to war with Russia, Turkey would come to our aid and probably close the Bosporus and Dardanelles, denying Russia access to the naval bases and ports in the Black Sea. That is the whole purpose of alliances, but sometimes they do not work! Both the Tigris and Euphrates rivers have their headwaters in Turkey.

Cyprus is a truly divided island country. Claimed by both Greece and Turkey, there is a great deal of hostility and bloodshed. Syria, Lebanon, Israel and Jordan are involved in an ongoing war over territory and religion. Did you know that the wife of the late King Hussein of Jordan was American and went to Princeton University?

## Saudi Arabia, Yemen, Oman, UAE, Qatar, Bahrain, Kuwait

Let's move on to the next seven countries:

| | | | |
|---|---|---|---|
| 13. Saudi Arabia | Riyadh | 17. Qatar | Doha |
| 14. Yemen | Sanaa | 18. Bahrain | Manama |
| 15. Oman | Muscat | 19. Kuwait | Kuwait City |
| 16. United Arab Emirates | Abu Dhabi | | |

These seven countries are all on the Arabian Peninsula and many have massive oil reserves. That's what the Gulf War in 1991 was all about, preventing Iraq from taking over the huge oil reserves in Kuwait.

Be sure to go over these countries at least five times daily. Write them down and check for spelling. Close your eyes and find their relative location. Use your mind. You don't want to be dependent on a map all the time when you have such a powerful tool between your ears!

## Iraq and Iran

Iraq and Iran can stand alone. Tehran, Iran and Baghdad, Iraq. I could never keep straight which one was the biggest, so I decided *Ron ran* long distances in *Iran*. That way both pronunciations of Tehran are covered! Remember, the Tigris and Euphrates flow through Iraq. So, there are *rocks* in the rivers which some people keep on *racks*. This covers both pronunciations of Iraq.

You should stop here and take a test over Southwest Asia and the connecting countries. Correct your spelling as you go along. Remember the connection between the hand and the eye is the most powerful learning tool. Write and write and write! Continually close your eyes and find each of these countries in your mental maps as well! When you have mastered Southwest Asia, combine it with the Soviet bloc countries for a larger test. Again check for spelling. Some of these letter combinations are very difficult but will come in time with practice.

Lets us look at the important role rivers play as natural boundaries. Absence of water is important because use of the land is severely curtailed. So always look for the presence and absence of rivers! It is always fun to talk about perceptions as you study a new area. Perceptions change with knowledge.

## Afghanistan, Pakistan, India, Sri Lanka, Nepal, Bhutan, Bangladesh, Myanmar

Countries and capitals of South Central Asia. Do you see why we named this South Central Asia? It is in the central part of the continent but also to the south. I felt it clarified relative location. Our connecting countries are the former Soviet bloc countries of Tajikistan, Uzbekistan and Turkmenistan to the north and Iran to the west.

The countries of South Central Asia and their capitals are:

| | | | |
|---|---|---|---|
| 5. Afghanistan | Kabul | 9. Nepal | Kathmandu |
| 6. Pakistan | Islamabad | 10. Bhutan | Thimphu |
| 7. India | New Delhi | 11. Bangladesh | Dhaka |
| 8. Sri Lanka | Colombo | 12. Myanmar | Rangoon |

Review the four connecting countries, then link them to Afghanistan, Pakistan and India, please. Sri Lanka is the little tear-drop shaped island at the southeastern tip of India. Unfortunately, the fighting between the Tamil Hindu minority and the Sinhalese Buddhist majority has almost destroyed this beautiful tropical island.

## Nepal, Bhutan, Bangladesh, Myanmar

Notice how Nepal, Bhutan, Bangladesh and Myanmar are all grouped together. Nine of the ten highest mountain peaks in the world are located in Nepal, including Mt. Everest. Nine out of every ten Nepalese are subsistence farmers, which mean they barely raise enough food to stay alive. In order to expand their farmlands, they cut down the trees on the sides of the Himalayas, with disastrous results. With the trees gone, there is nothing to hold the soil in place on the steep sides of the mountains. So, as the rains fall and the winds blow, the soil is carried away, much of it destroying land farther downstream in Bhutan and Bangladesh.

Bangladesh has the lowest elevation of any country in the world, so when a monsoon comes, the country floods. Myanmar is one of those well placed connecting countries. It sits right next to India and Bangladesh. In fact, before Myanmar changed its name there were three countries in a row all beginning with B: Bhutan, Bangladesh and Burma.

## Mongolia and China

Mongolia has the world's coldest, northernmost desert, the Gobi. Only 5% of the Gobi is covered with sand dunes. China is the world's most populous country with 20% of the world's population. It is also second only to Saudi Arabia in oil reserves!

## Laos, Thailand, Cambodia, Vietnam, Malaysia

Remember the movie "The King and I"? Well, Thailand was formerly known as Siam, and it was the King of Siam in the movie.

Laos, Cambodia and Vietnam are the three countries previously known as French Indochina. Malaysia is on the Malay Peninsula, as well as part of the island of Borneo.

## Singapore, Brunei, Indonesia, Philippines, East Timor

The richest man in the world is the Sultan of Brunei! One way to remember the correct spelling of the Philippines is *Philip pines* (this helps to remember there is only one *l* but two *p*'s). There are three countries on the island of Borneo. They are  Malaysia, Brunei and Indonesia.

East Timor became an independent nation on May 20, 2002.

## Taiwan, Japan, North Korea, South Korea

Taiwan, Japan and South Korea are strong industrial export nations with many personal and religious freedoms. North Korea is a repressive communist nation with a very weak economy and severe starvation at this time due to drought. Most of North Korea's income is spent on their military and many fear they will start a war with South Korea to ease their economic problems.

# Pronunciation Guide: Former Soviet Republics and Capitals (Map #3)

1. Moscow, Russia   mŏs´kō, rŭsh´ə
2. Tbilisi, Georgia   tə-bə-lē´sē, jôr´jə
3. Yerevan, Armenia   yĕ´rĭ-vän´, är-mē´nē-ə
4. Baku, Azerbaijan   bä-kōō´, äh´zĕr-bĭ-jän´
5. Ashgabat, Turkmenistan   äsh´kə-bät´, tûrk´mĕ-nə-stän´
6. Tashkent, Uzbekistan   tăsh-kĕnt´, ŏŏz-bĕk´ĭ-stän´
7. Dushanbe, Tajikistan   dōō-shăm´bə, tä-jĭk´ĭ-stän´
8. Bishkek, Kyrgyzstan   bĭsh´kĕk, kîr´gĭ-stän´
9. Almaty, Kazakhstan   əl-mä´tē, kə-zäk´stän

# Pronunciation Guide: Southwest Asia Countries and Capitals (Map #5)

1. Cairo, Egypt   kī´rō, ē´jĭpt
2. Khartoum, Sudan   kär-tōōm´, sōō-dăn´
3. Asmara, Eritrea   ăz-mä´rə, ĕr´ĭ-trē´ə
4. Addis Ababa, Ethiopia   ăd´ĭs äb´ə-bə, ē´thē-ō´pē-ə
5. Djibouti, Djibouti   jĭ-bōō´tē, jĭ-bōō´tē
6. Mogadishu, Somalia   mŏg´ə-dĭsh´-ōō, sō-mä´lē-ə
7. Ankara, Turkey   ăng´kər-ə, tûr´kē
8. Nicosia, Cyprus   nĭk´ə-sē´ə, sī´prĭs
9. Damascus, Syria   də-măs´kəs, sîr´ē-ə
10. Beirut, Lebanon   bā-rōōt´, lĕb´ə-nən
11. Jerusalem, Israel   jĭ-rōō´sə-ləm, ĭz´rē-əl
12. Amman, Jordan   ä-män´, jôr´dn
13. Riyadh, Saudi Arabia   rē-yäd´, sou´dē ə-rā´bē-ə
14. Sanaa, Yemen   sä´na, yĕm´ən
15. Muscat, Oman   mŭs-kăt´, ō-män´
16. Abu Dhabi, United Arab Emirates   ä´bōō dä´bē, yōō-nī´tĭd ăr´əb ĕm´ər-ĭts
17. Doha, Qatar   dō´hə, kä-tär´
18. Manama, Bahrain   mə-năm´ə, bä-rān´
19. Kuwait City, Kuwait   kōō-wāt´ sĭt´ē, kōō-wāt´
20. Baghdad, Iraq   băg´dăd, ĭ-răk´
21. Tehran, Iran   tĕ´ə-răn´, ĭ-răn´

| ă pat | oi boy |
|---|---|
| ā pay | ou out |
| âr care | ŏŏ tŏŏk |
| ä father | ōō bōōt |
| ĕ pet | ŭ cut |
| ē be | ûr urge |
| ĭ pit | th thin |
| ī pie | *th* this |
| îr pier | hw which |
| ŏ pot | zh vision |
| ō toe | ə about |
| ô paw | item |

**Stress marks:**
´ (primary);
´ (secondary), as in
**dictionary (dĭk´shə-nĕr´ē)**

# Pronunciation Guide: Rivers of Southwest Asia (Map #6)

1. Nile   **nīl**
2. Blue Nile   **blōō nīl**
3. White Nile   **wīt nīl**
4. Jordan   **jôr´dn**
5. Tigris   **tī´grĭs**
6. Euphrates   **yōō-frā´tēz**
7. Kizil   **kĭ-zĭl´**
8. Araks   **ə-räks´**

# Pronunciation Guide: South Central Asia countries and capitals (Map #7)

1. Dushanbe, Tajikistan   **dōō-shăm´bə, tä-jĭk´ĭ-stän´**
2. Tashkent, Uzbekistan   **tăsh-kĕnt´, ŏŏz-bĕk´ĭ-stän´**
3. Ashgabat, Turkmenistan   **äsh´kə-bät´, tûrk´mĕ-nə-stän´**
4. Tehran, Iran   **tĕ´ə-răn´, ĭ-răn´**
5. Kabul, Afghanistan   **kä´bŏŏl, ăf-găn´ĭ-stän´**
6. Islamabad, Pakistan   **ĭs-lä´mə-băd´ păk´ĭ-stän´**
7. New Delhi, India   **nōō dĕl´ē, ĭn´dē-ə**
8. Colombo, Sri Lanka   **kə-lŭm´bō, srē läng´kə**
9. Kathmandu, Nepal   **kăt´măn-dōō´, nə-pôl´**
10. Beijing, China   **bā´jĭng´, chī´nə**
11. Thimphu, Bhutan   **thĭm´pōō´, bōō-tăn´**
12. Dhaka, Bangladesh   **dăk´ə, băng´glə-dĕsh´**
13. Rangoon, Myanmar   **răn-gōōn´, myän-mär´**

# Pronunciation Guide: Rivers of South Central Asia (Map #8)

1. Amu Darya   **ä´mōō där´yə**
2. Indus   **ĭn´dəs**
3. Ganges   **găn´jēz´**
4. Brahmaputra   **brä´mə-pōō´trə**
5. Irrawaddy   **îr´ə-wŏd´ē**

| ă pat | oi boy |
|---|---|
| ā pay | ou out |
| âr care | ŏŏ tŏŏk |
| ä father | ōō bōōt |
| ĕ pet | ŭ cut |
| ē be | ûr urge |
| ĭ pit | th thin |
| ī pie | *th* this |
| îr pier | hw which |
| ŏ pot | zh vision |
| ō toe | ə about |
| ô paw | item |

**Stress marks:**
´ (primary);
´ (secondary), as in
**dictionary (dĭk´shə-nĕr´ē)**

# Pronunciation Guide: Southeast Asia Countries and Capitals (Map #9)

1. Moscow, Russia  **mŏs´kō, rŭsh´ə**
2. Ulan Bator, Mongolia  **o͞o´län bä´tôr, mŏng-gō´lē-ə**
3. Beijing, China  **bā´jĭng´, chĭ´nə**
4. Rangoon, Myanmar (Burma)  **răng-go͞on´, myän-mär (bûr-mə)**
5. Vientiane, Laos  **vyĕn-tyän´, lä´ŏs´**
6. Bangkok, Thailand  **băng´kŏk´, tī´lănd**
7. Phnom Penh, Cambodia  **pə-nôm´pĕn´, kăm-bō´dē-ə**
8. Hanoi, Vietnam  **hă-noi´, vē-ĕt´näm´**
9. Kuala Lumpur, Malaysia  **kwä´lə lo͝om-po͝or´, mə-lā´zhə**
10. Singapore, Singapore  **sĭng´ə-pôr´, sĭng´ə-pôr´**
11. Bandar Seri Begawan, Brunei  **bŭn´dər sĕr´ē bə-gä´wən, bro͞o-nĭ´**
12. Jakarta, Indonesia  **jə-kär´tə, ĭn´də-nē´zhə**
13. Manilla, Philippines  **mə-nĭl´ə, fĭl´ə-pēnz´**
14. Taipei, Taiwan  **tī´pā´, tī´wän´**
15. Tokyo, Japan  **tō´kē-ō´, jə-păn´**
16. Pyongyang, North Korea  **pyŭng´yäng´, nôrth kə-rē´ə**
17. Seoul, South Korea  **sōl, south kə-rē´ə**
18. Dili, East Timor  **dē´lē, ēst tē´môr**

# Pronunciation Guide: Rivers of East Asia (Map #10)

1. Mekong  **mā´kông´**
2. Irrawaddy  **îr´ə-wŏd´ē**
3. Salween  **săl´wēn´**
4. Chao Phraya  **chou prä-yä´**
5. Yangtze  **yăng´sē´**
6. Hwang He  **hwäng´hĕ´**
7. Yalu  **yä´lo͞o´**
8. Argun  **är-go͞on´**
9. Amur  **ä-mo͞or´**

| | |
|---|---|
| ă pat | oi boy |
| ā pay | ou out |
| âr care | o͝o to͝ok |
| ä father | o͞o bo͞ot |
| ĕ pet | ŭ cut |
| ē be | ûr urge |
| ĭ pit | th thin |
| ī pie | *th* this |
| îr pier | hw which |
| ŏ pot | zh vision |
| ō toe | ə about |
| ô paw | item |

**Stress marks:**
´ (primary);
´ (secondary), as in
**dictionary (dĭk´shə-nĕr´ē)**

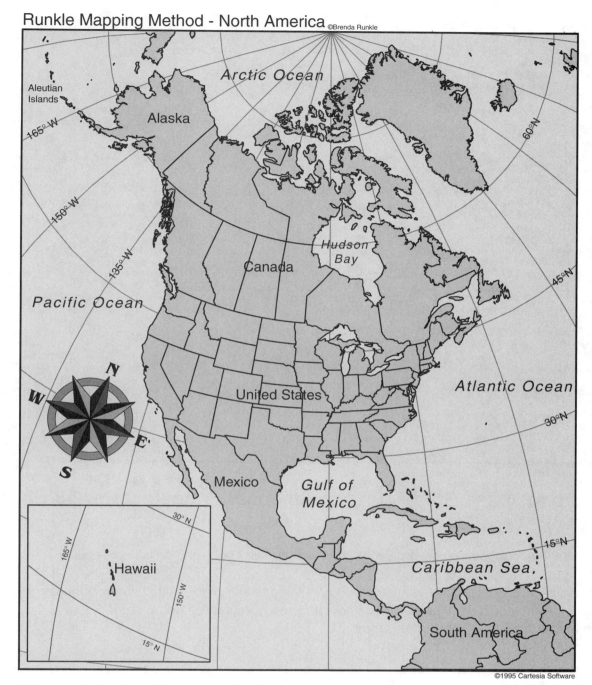

©1995 Cartesia Software

# Map #1 in the Study of North America: Relative Location

- Europe and the Atlantic Ocean to the east
- South America to the southeast
- Asia to the west
- Arctic Ocean to the North
- Aleutian Islands to the northwest
- Gulf of Mexico and Caribbean Sea to the south
- Pacific Ocean to the west

North America lies north of the equator, west of the prime meridian, and east of the 180th meridian of longitude, placing it in three hemispheres, Northern, Western and Eastern. The volcanic Aleutian Islands extend 1700 miles west from Alaska and separate the Bering Sea from the Pacific Ocean.

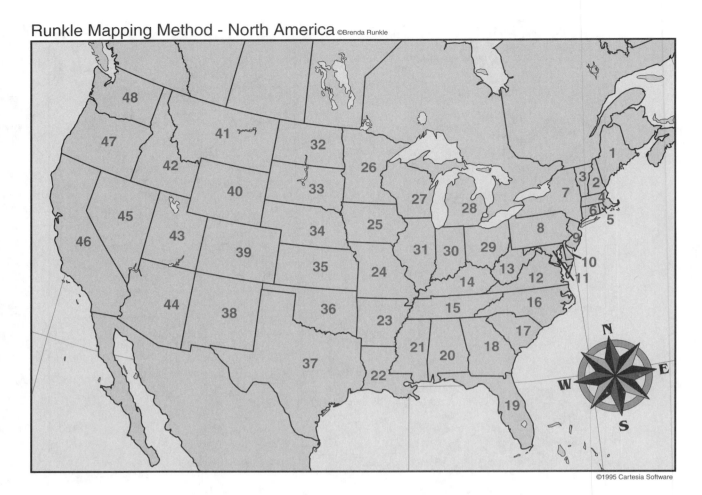

©1995 Cartesia Software

# Map #2 in the Study of North America: Pretest, Lower 48 States

Use this map to become familiar with the contiguous states of the United States.

It is always fun to take a test before you begin something new so that you can measure your progress as you learn. Take a pretest now and see how many states you can name at this point in time. Map #3 will identify the states.

Did you notice Alaska and Hawaii do not show on this map? These are the contiguous 48 states. Contiguous means having a common border.  So these states are all joined by common borders.  They are known as the "Lower 48". Alaska is separated from the contiguous 48 states by Canada, and Hawaii is in the middle of the Pacific Ocean. Thus, they do not share a common border with the other states.

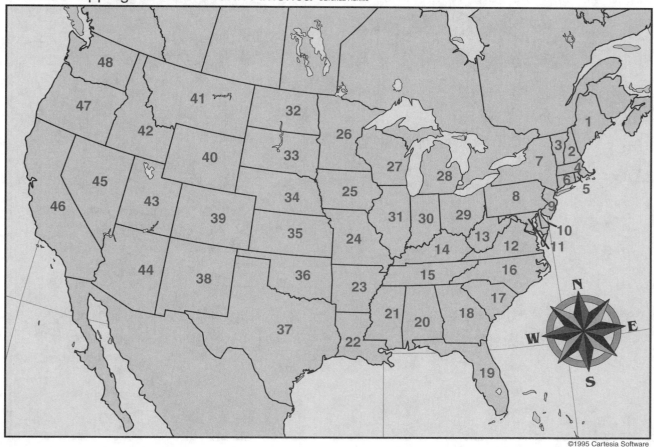

©1995 Cartesia Software

# Map #3 in the Study of North America: The 48 Contiguous US States

| | | |
|---|---|---|
| 1. Maine | 17. South Carolina | 33. South Dakota |
| 2. New Hampshire | 18. Georgia | 34. Nebraska |
| 3. Vermont | 19. Florida | 35. Kansas |
| 4. Massachusetts | 20. Alabama | 36. Oklahoma |
| 5. Rhode Island | 21. Mississippi | 37. Texas |
| 6. Connecticut | 22. Louisiana | 38. New Mexico |
| 7. New York | 23. Arkansas | 39. Colorado |
| 8. Pennsylvania | 24. Missouri | 40. Wyoming |
| 9. New Jersey | 25. Iowa | 41. Montana |
| 10. Delaware | 26. Minnesota | 42. Idaho |
| 11. Maryland | 27. Wisconsin | 43. Utah |
| 12. Virginia | 28. Michigan | 44. Arizona |
| 13. West Virginia | 29. Ohio | 45. Nevada |
| 14. Kentucky | 30. Indiana | 46. California |
| 15. Tennessee | 31. Illinois | 47. Oregon |
| 16. North Carolina | 32. North Dakota | 48. Washington |

©1995 Cartesia Software

# Map #4 in the Study of North America: The 48 Contiguous US States

Beginning in the northeast, names and abbreviations of the states are:

| | | | | | |
|---|---|---|---|---|---|
| ME | Maine | SC | South Carolina | SD | South Dakota |
| NH | New Hampshire | GA | Georgia | NE | Nebraska |
| VT | Vermont | FL | Florida | KS | Kansas |
| MA | Massachusetts | AL | Alabama | OK | Oklahoma |
| RI | Rhode Island | MS | Mississippi | TX | Texas |
| CT | Connecticut | LA | Louisiana | NM | New Mexico |
| NY | New York | AR | Arkansas | CO | Colorado |
| PA | Pennsylvania | MO | Missouri | WY | Wyoming |
| NJ | New Jersey | IA | Iowa | MT | Montana |
| DE | Delaware | MN | Minnesota | ID | Idaho |
| MD | Maryland | WI | Wisconsin | UT | Utah |
| VA | Virginia | MI | Michigan | AZ | Arizona |
| WV | West Virginia | OH | Ohio | NV | Nevada |
| KY | Kentucky | IN | Indiana | CA | California |
| TN | Tennessee | IL | Illinois | OR | Oregon |
| NC | North Carolina | ND | North Dakota | WA | Washington |

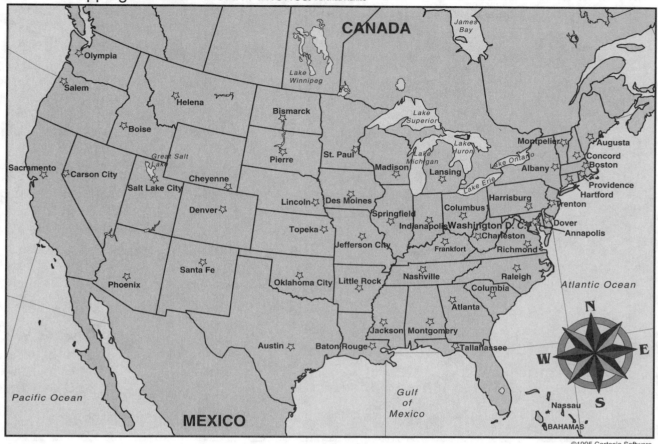

©1995 Cartesia Software

## Map #5 in the Study of North America: State Capitals

Match the capitals with the correct state names.

The capital of Hawaii is Honolulu.
The capital of Alaska is Juneau.

Juneau, Alaska is located at 58° N 134°W and Olympia Washington is located at 47° N 123° W. Honolulu, Hawaii is located at 21° N 158° W and Austin Texas is located at 30° N 80° W. This should help you to visualize just how far Hawaii and Alaska are from the other 48 states.

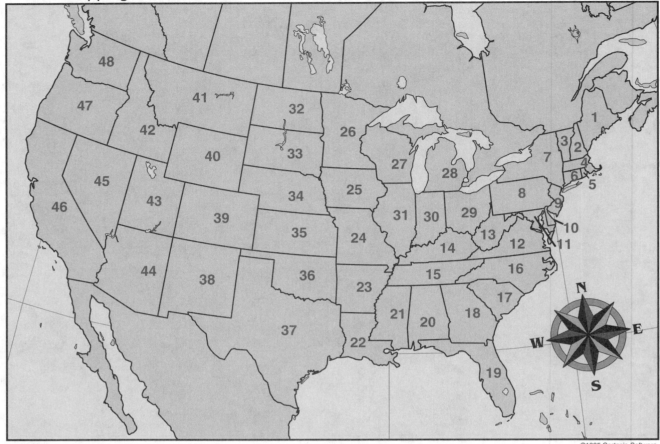

©1995 Cartesia Software

## Map #6 in the Study of North America: Test of the United States

On a clean sheet of paper, list the numbers 1-50. Two of the states do not show on this map, but have questions about their location. Write the name of each state beside its corresponding number. Next to the name of each state, write its capital. For number 49 name the state that is farthest north and does not have a common border with the other 48 states. For number 50 name the state that is a series of volcanic islands in the Pacific. Be sure to check your spelling. One of the marks of a well educated person is correct spelling. For each name you misspell, please write it correctly ten times, or until you are confident that you have mastered the correct spelling. Remember, the hand and the eye make a great team in helping you to learn!

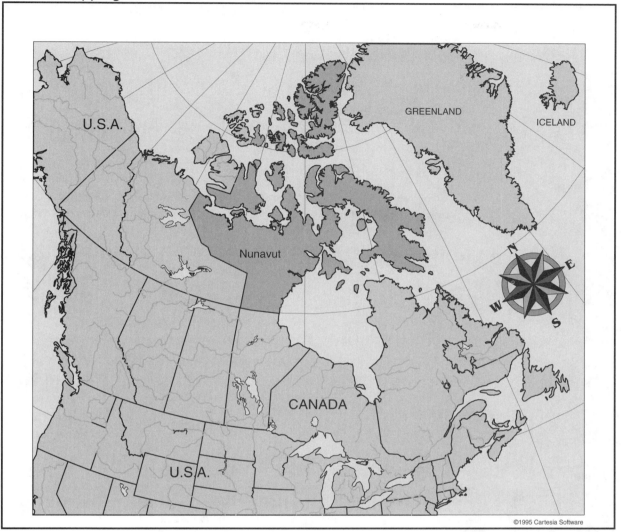

## Map #7 in the Study of North America: Relative Location of Canada

- United States to the south
- Alaska to the northwest
- Arctic Ocean to the north
- Pacific Ocean to the west
- Atlantic Ocean to the east

On April 1, 1999, Canada turned over approximately 770,000 square miles of the Northwest Territories to the Inuit. This new territory is called Nunavut, "our land" in the Inuit language. No longer called Eskimos in Canada, the Inuit now have direct ownership over 13,896 square miles of Nunavut. This is not a reservation, rather an open democracy just like any other province or territory in Canada. Nunavut occupies nearly 70% of the Northwest Territories, with a population of only 17,500. The 3,000-mile long border between Canda and the United States is the world's longest undefended border.

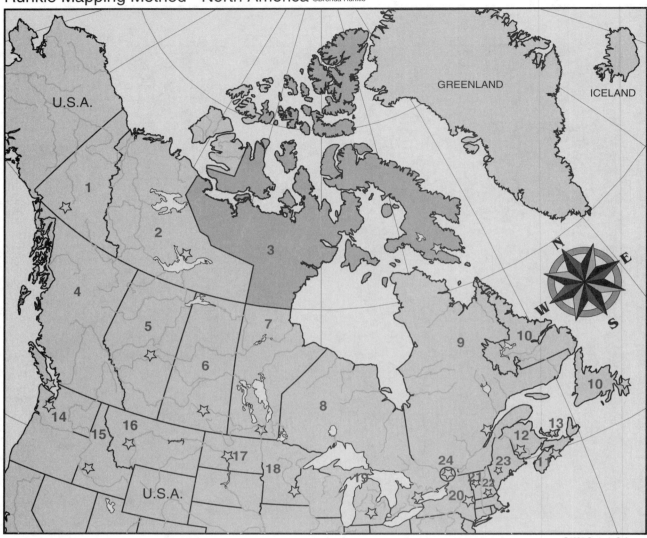

©1995 Cartesia Software

# Map #8 in the Study of North America: The 13 Provinces and Territories of Canada, Bordering U.S. States and their Capitals

1. Whitehorse, Yukon Territory
2. Yellowknife, Northwest Territories
3. Iqaluit, Nunavut
4. Victoria, British Columbia
5. Edmonton, Alberta
6. Regina, Saskatchewan
7. Winnipeg, Manitoba
8. Toronto, Ontario
9. Quebec, Quebec
10. St. John's, Newfoundland
11. Halifax, Nova Scotia
12. Fredericton, New Brunswick

13. Charlottetown, Prince Edward Island
14. Olympia, Washington
15. Boise, Idaho
16. Helena, Montana
17. Bismarck, North Dakota
18. St. Paul, Minnesota
19. Lansing, Michigan
20. Albany, New York
21. Montpelier, Vermont
22. Concord, New Hampshire
23. Augusta, Maine
24. Ottawa, Canada

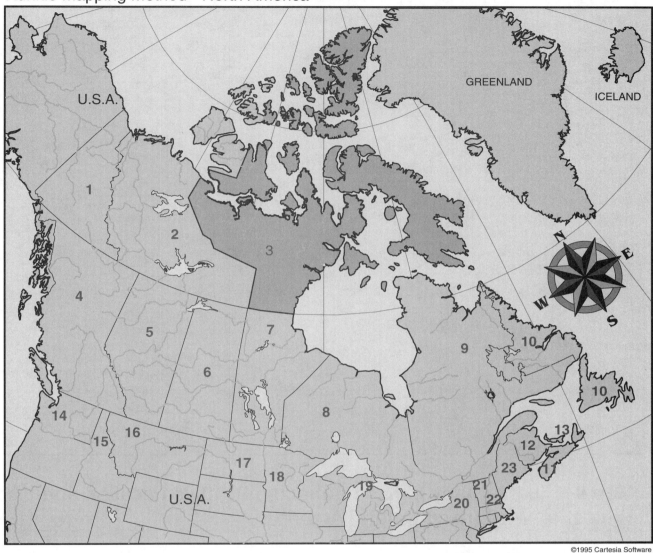

GREENLAND

ICELAND

U.S.A.

U.S.A.

N
E
W
S

©1995 Cartesia Software

# Map #9 in the Study of North America: Canada Map Test

On a clean sheet of paper, list the numbers 1-23. Write the name of the Canadian province or territory or bordering U.S. state beside each corresponding number. Next to the name of the province, territory or U.S. state, write the name of its capital. Be sure to check your spelling. For each name you misspell, please write it ten times correctly, or until you are confident that you have mastered the correct spelling.

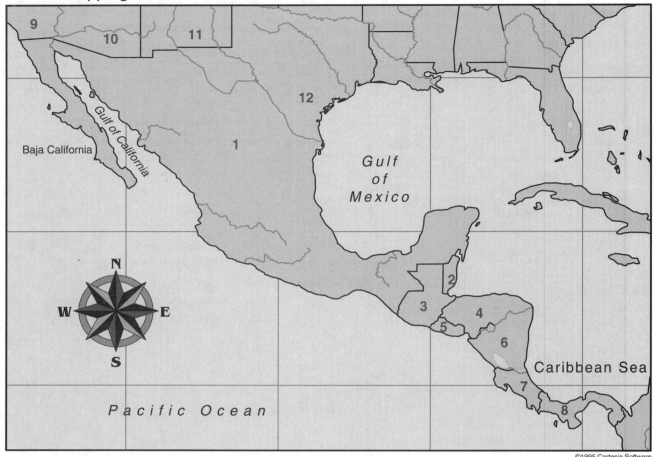

©1995 Cartesia Software

# Map #10 in the Study of North America: Relative Location and Pretest of Mexico and Central America

• United States to the north
• Pacific Ocean to the west and south
• Gulf of Mexico to the east
• South America to the southeast

Use this map to become familiar with all of Mexico and Central America. It is always fun to take a test before you begin something new so that you can measure your progress as you learn. Take a pretest now and see how many of the countries of Mexico and Central America you can name at this point in time. Map #11 will identify the countries.

Fun Fact: The Gulf of California is also known as the Sea of Cortez.

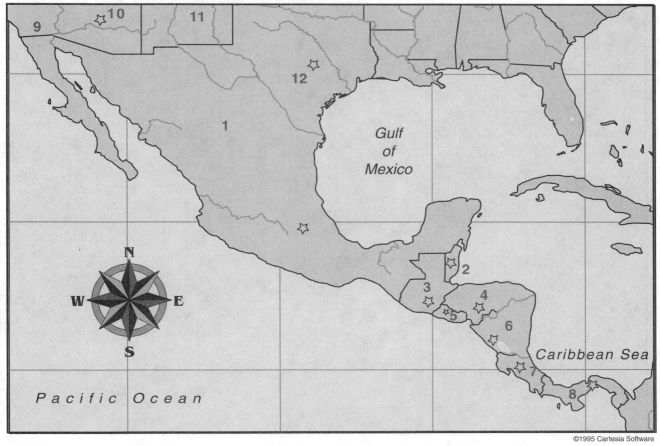

©1995 Cartesia Software

## Map #11 in the Study of North America: The 8 Countries of Mexico and Central America, and the Bordering U.S. States, and Capitals

1. Mexico City, Mexico
2. Belmopan, Belize
3. Guatemala City, Guatemala
4. Tegucigalpa, Honduras

5. San Salvador, El Salvador
6. Managua, Nicaragua
7. San Jose, Costa Rica
8. Panama, Panama

9. Sacramento, California
10. Phoenix, Arizona
11. Santa Fe, New Mexico
12. Austin, Texas

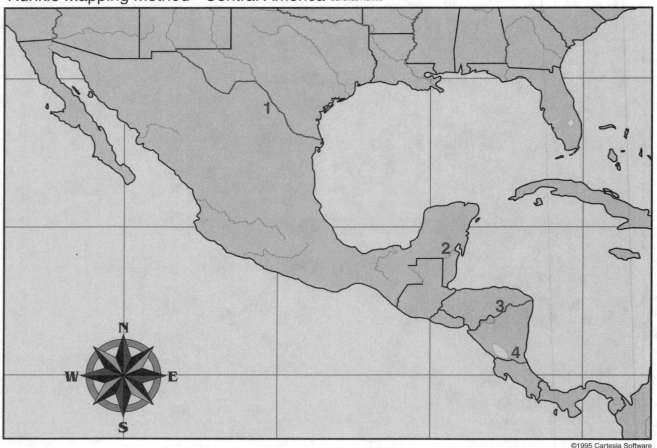

©1995 Cartesia Software

## Map #12 in the Study of North America: Boundary Rivers of Mexico and Central America:

1. Rio Grande            2. Hondo            3. Coco            4. San Juan

Use this map of Mexico and Central America to determine where a river forms a boundary between countries, please. This is a critical thinking skill activity to help you develop your powers of observation. Called natural boundaries, these rivers will play an important role throughout history as they affect the movement of people, goods and ideas. A natural boundary will be visible to the eye, form a barrier of some sort and be easily recognized.

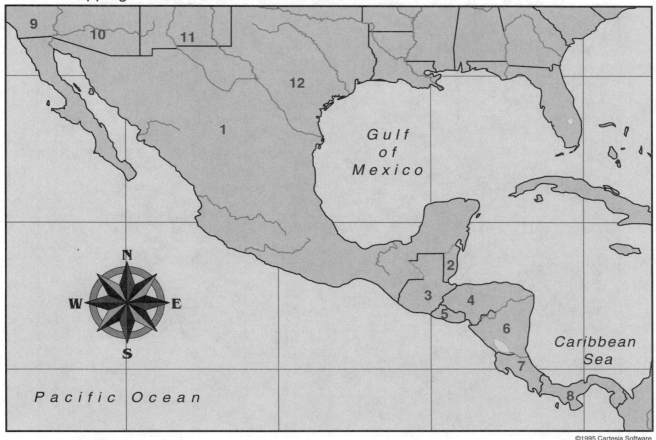

©1995 Cartesia Software

## Map #13 in the Study of North America: Mexico and Central America Map Test

On a clean sheet of paper, list the numbers 1-12. Write the name of each country or bordering US state beside each corresponding number. Next to the name of the country or state, write the name of its capital. Be sure to check your spelling. One of the marks of a well educated person is correct spelling. For each name you misspell, please write it ten times correctly, or until you are confident that you have mastered the correct spelling.

Arctic Ocean

Aleution
Islands

Beaufort Sea

Baffin Bay

Pacific Ocean

Labrador Sea

Hudson
Bay

Bermuda

Atlantic Ocean

Gulf
of
Mexico

Hawaii

30° N

165° W

150° W

15° N

Caribbean Sea

Lake
Nicaragua

©1995 Cartesia Software

# Map #14 in the Study of North America: Enrichment Activity

Use this map of North America to determine where a state or international boundary is formed by a river.  For now, you should see how many rivers you can identify on your own. It is important to be aware of physical features that form boundaries. These natural boundaries have played an important role throughout history as they affect the movement of people, goods and ideas. Natural boundaries will be visible to the eye, form a barrier of some sort and be easily recognized. Thus, they make good national and international boundaries. Map #15 will identify each of these rivers.

Artic Ocean

Aleutian Islands

U.S.A.

Beaufort Sea

ICELAND

GREENLAND

Baffin Bay

150°W

135° W

Labrador Sea

Pacific Ocean

Hudson Bay

CANADA

Gulf of St. Lawrence

Lake Superior

Lake Huron

7

4

Lake Michigan

Lake Ontario

8

3

Lake Erie

U.S.A.

5    6

9

2

Bermuda

11

4

12

Atlantic Ocean

10

MEXICO

Gulf of Mexico

BAHAMAS

CUBA

DOM. REP.

BELIZE

JAMAICA

HAITI

GUATEMALA

HONDURAS

Caribbean Sea

EL SALVADOR

NICARAGUA

Lake Nicaragua

COSTA RICA

VENEZUELA

GUYANA

PANAMA

COLOMBIA

BRAZIL

Hawaii

30° N

165° W

150° W

15° N

©1995 Cartesia Software

# Map #15  in the Study of North America: Boundary Rivers

| | | |
|---|---|---|
| 1. Columbia | 5. Wabash | 9. Red |
| 2. Snake | 6. Ohio | 10. Rio Grande |
| 3. Missouri | 7. Ottawa | 11. Colorado |
| 4. Mississippi | 8. Connecticut | 12. Chattahoochee |

# Learning North America the Easy Way!

Let's begin by learning the 48 contiguous states of the United States of America. I strongly encourage you to learn all the state capitals.

## Maine, New Hampshire, Vermont, New York, Massachusetts, Rhode Island, Connecticut

Without New York, the other six states make up the region known as New England. This is poor, rocky, cold, glaciated land. The fences of rock bear mute testimony to the work of glaciers. Many geographers believe that if America had been settled from the West, New England would have remained unsettled!

## Pennsylvania, New Jersey, Delaware, Maryland, Virginia

Can you guess where the Delmarva Peninsula is? It is part of Delaware, Maryland and Virginia and separates Chesapeake Bay from Delaware Bay and the Atlantic Ocean.

Our national capital, Washington, D.C., is located on the Potomac River, which empties into Chesapeake Bay. The Mason-Dixon line is the boundary between Pennsylvania and Maryland. It is also the dividing line between the North and the South.

Go over each of these states at least five times each day. Go over them in the same order until you can close your eyes and find them in your mind. Keep in mind their relative location, too. For instance, when you were looking at your map, did you notice which states bordered the Great Lakes and which bordered Canada? Pay attention to important details like that.

## West Virginia, Kentucky, Tennessee, North Carolina, South Carolina, Georgia

The Appalachian Mountains run through parts of each of these states. Coal, natural gas and forests are abundant in these states. The Tennessee Valley Authority provides hydroelectric energy to this region by damming the Tennessee River and its tributaries.

## Florida, Alabama, Mississippi, Louisiana

These four states all have coasts along the Gulf of Mexico.

## Arkansas, Missouri, Iowa, Minnesota

These four states form a line to the north, from the hills of Arkansas to the plains and into the Great Lakes region.

## Wisconsin, Michigan, Ohio, Indiana, Illinois

These five states all have borders along the Great Lakes.

## North Dakota, South Dakota, Nebraska, Kansas, Oklahoma, Texas

These are the Great Plains states from the Canadian border south to the Gulf of Mexico. Some Texans say the only thing between them and Canada is a barbed wire fence! Great farmland.

## New Mexico, Colorado, Wyoming, Montana, Idaho

Here you find deserts in the south, and mountains all the way to the Canadian border. This is beautiful land.

## Utah, Arizona, Nevada, California, Oregon, Washington

From the Great Salt Lake and the Painted Desert to the beautiful mountains and rugged Pacific coast!

# Learning Canada the Easy Way!

Now let's learn about Canada. Here is a funny story I made up many years ago to teach my students the provinces, territories and capitals of Canada.

## Yukon Territory, Northwest Territories, British Columbia, Alberta, Saskatchewan, Manitoba

We left the *Yukon Territory* on our *Whitehorse* to go get our *Yellowknife* in the *Northwest Territories*. Then we went to *British Columbia* to see Queen *Victoria*. We then went east to see her husband *Alberta* and son, *Edmonton*. On the way to *Regina* I heard an old Indian say *Sas kat chew an*! Wonder what he meant! Later, I heard him say "*Man i tob a, Win ni peg*, or don't come home." Think he meant to say, "Man I told ya, win a pig or don't come home"? Who knows?

## Ontario, Quebec, Newfoundland, Prince Edward Island, Novia Scotia, New Brunswick

I'll bet Tonto never went to *Toronto*, even if he was in *Ontario*.
*Quebec*, *Quebec* what the heck!
Have you ever been to *St. John's, Newfoundland*?
*Prince Edward* went to *Charlottetown* last year. Next thing I knew he got into trouble by saying *Halifax* in *Nova Scotia*! Then his friend *Fredericton* bought him new tires in *New Brunswick* and they went back home!

Here are some facts about our neighbor to the north. The national capital is Ottawa in Ontario. Canada has never had a civil war or widespread slavery. Although Canada extends into the Arctic, about 90% of its people live along the U.S.-Canadian border.

Look at the map and figure this one out! The southernmost part of Canada is south of the northern-most part of Pennsylvania! And it lies only 138 miles from the Mason-Dixon Line, which is the dividing line between Maryland and Pennsylvania. This is also considered to be the dividing line between our North and South!

Isn't it odd that you have to go north from Windsor, Ontario, Canada to get to Detroit, Michigan?

# Learning Central America the Easy Way!

There are only 8 countries on the isthmus of Central America. An isthmus is a narrow neck of land connecting two larger land masses. In other words, an isthmus serves as a land bridge.

## Mexico, Belize, Guatemala

Let's begin in the north with the largest country, Mexico. Notice it is bordered on the north by the United States and to the south by Belize and Guatemala. The finger of land to the west is Baja California. The sea dividing the mainland from the Baja Peninsula is known to the Mexicans as the Sea of Cortez but to us as the Gulf of California. Mountains border the central plateau where the capital, Mexico City, is located. This city has the most polluted air in the world. In fact, it is so bad that in 1991, school children were not allowed to leave for school until the rush hour traffic was over and they had to be home before the evening rush hour began. Breathing the air was the same as smoking two packs of cigarettes a day! Mexico City may well be the largest city in the world by the end of this century. Most of its population is either very, very rich or very, very poor!

Belize was known as British Honduras until it gained independence in 1981. It is the least populated of the Central American countries and the only one with English as the official language and Protestantism as the majority religion. The world's second largest barrier reef lies 8 to 25 miles offshore.

Most of the people living in Guatemala are Indians. Blessed with fertile volcanic soil and a thriving middle class, it is also a country of terrible poverty for the majority of the population. This has led to an ongoing civil war between brutal dictators and opposition parties.

## Honduras, El Salvador, Nicaragua, Costa Rica, Panama

Honduras is one of the "banana republics" whose chief export is bananas, of course! The famous Mosquito Coast lies along the Caribbean side. By the way, the Mosquitos were Indians, not insects!

El Salvador is the smallest country and, along with Guatemala, the only one without a Caribbean coast. The capital, San Salvador, has been destroyed numerous times by earthquakes.

Nicaragua has been beseiged by civil war, brutal dictatorships and political murders. It has the largest per-capita foreign debt in the world, most of which went to support the military. The capital of Managua is also prone to earthquakes.

Costa Rica is the most European of all the countries in Central America. It is also the most stable, with no standing army, high education standards and good medical care. The people get along well and ownership of land is widespread.

The Panama Canal was completed by the United States in 1914 and it has made Panama an important player in international shipping. Prior to the building of the canal, Panama was claimed by Colombia. In fact, many people think Panama ought to be considered a South American country due to its historical relationship with Colombia.

# Pronunciation Guide: The 50 United States (Map #3)

1. Maine  **mān**
2. New Hampshire  **nōō hămp´shər**
3. Vermont  **vər-mŏnt´**
4. Massachusetts  **măs´ə-chōō´sĭts**
5. Rhode Island  **rōd ī´lənd**
6. Connecticut  **kə-nĕt´ĭ-kət**
7. New York  **nōō yôrk**
8. Pennsylvania  **pĕn´səl-vān´yə**
9. New Jersey  **nōō jûr´zē**
10. Delaware  **dĕl´ə-wâr´**
11. Maryland  **mĕr´ə-lənd**
12. Virginia  **vər-jĭn´yə**
13. West Virginia  **wĕst vər-jĭn´yə**
14. Kentucky  **kən-tŭk´ē**
15. Tennessee  **tĕn´ĭ-sē´**
16. North Carolina  **nôrth kar´ə-lī´nə**
17. South Carolina  **south kar´ə-lī´nə**
18. Georgia  **jôr´jə**
19. Florida  **flôr´ĭ-də**
20. Alabama  **ăl´ə-băm´ə**
21. Mississippi  **mĭs´ĭ-sĭp´ē**
22. Louisiana  **lōō-ē´zē-ăn´ə**
23. Arkansas  **är´kən-sô´**
24. Missouri  **mĭ-zŏŏ´rē**
25. Iowa  **ī´ə-wə**
26. Minnesota  **mĭn´ĭ-sō´tə**
27. Wisconsin  **wĭs-kŏn´sĭn**
28. Michigan  **mĭsh´ĭ-gən**
29. Ohio  **ō-hī´ō**
30. Indiana  **ĭn´dē-ăn´ə**
31. Illinois  **ĭl´ə-noi´**
32. North Dakota  **nôrth də-kō´tə**
33. South Dakota  **south də-kō´tə**
34. Nebraska  **nə-brăs´kə**
35. Kansas  **kăns´əs**
36. Oklahoma  **ōk´lə-hō´mə**
37. Texas  **tĕk´səs**
38. New Mexico  **nōō mĕk´sĭ-kō´**
39. Colorado  **kŏl´ə-rä´dō**
40. Wyoming  **wī-ō´mĭng**
41. Montana  **mŏn-tăn´ə**
42. Idaho  **ī´də-hō´**
43. Utah  **yōō´tô´**
44. Arizona  **ăr´ĭ-zō´nə**
45. Nevada  **nə-văd´ə**
46. California  **kăl´ĭ-fôr´nyə**
47. Oregon  **ôr´ĭ-gən**
48. Washington  **wŏsh´ĭng-tən**
49. Hawaii  **hə-wä´ē**
50. Alaska  **ə-lăs´kə**

| | | | |
|---|---|---|---|
| ă | pat | oi | boy |
| ā | pay | ou | out |
| âr | care | ŏŏ | took |
| ä | father | ōō | boot |
| ĕ | pet | ŭ | cut |
| ē | be | ûr | urge |
| ĭ | pit | th | thin |
| ī | pie | *th* | this |
| îr | pier | hw | which |
| ŏ | pot | zh | vision |
| ō | toe | ə | about |
| ô | paw | | item |

**Stress marks:**
´ (primary);
´ (secondary), as in
**dictionary (dĭk´shə-nĕr´ē)**

79

# Pronunciation Guide: The 50 United States capitals (Map #5)

1. Augusta  ô-gŭs´tə
2. Concord  kŏn´kôrd
3. Montpelier  mŏnt-pēl´yər
4. Boston  bôs´tən
5. Providence  prŏv´i-dəns
6. Hartford  härt´fərd
7. Albany  ôl´bə-nē
8. Harrisburg  hăr´ĭs-bûrg´
9. Trenton  trĭn´tən
10. Dover  dō´vər
11. Baltimore  bôl´tĭ-môr´
12. Richmond  rĭch´mənd
13. Charleston  chärl´stən
14. Frankfort  frăngk´fərt
15. Nashville  năsh´vĭl´
16. Raleigh  rô´lē
17. Columbia  kə-lŭm´bē-ə
18. Atlanta  ăt-lăn´tə
19. Tallahassee  tăl´ə-hăs´ē
20. Montgomery  mŏnt-gŭm´ə-rē
21. Jackson  jăk´sən
22. Baton Rouge  băt´n rōōzh
23. Little Rock  lĭt´l rŏk
24. Jefferson City  jĕf´ĕr-sən sĭt´ē
25. Des Moines  dĕ moin´
26. Saint Paul  sānt pôl
27. Madison  măd´ĭ-sən
28. Lansing  lan´sĭng
29. Columbus  kə-lŭm´bəs
30. Indianapolis  ĭn´dē-ə-năp´ə-lĭs
31. Springfield  sprĭng´fēld
32. Bismarck  bĭz´märk
33. Pierre  pîr
34. Lincoln  lĭng´kən
35. Topeka  tə-pēk´ə
36. Oklahoma City  ōk´lə-hō´mə sĭt´ē
37. Austin  ô´stən
38. Santa Fe  săn´tə fā
39. Denver  dĕn´vər
40. Cheyenne  shĭ-ĕn´
41. Helena  hĕl´ə-nə
42. Boise  boi´zē
43. Salt Lake City  sôlt lāk´ sĭt´ē
44. Phoenix  fē´nĭks
45. Carson City  kär´sən sĭt´ē
46. Sacramento  săk´rə-mĕn´tō
47. Salem  sā´ləm
48. Olympia  ō-lĭm´pē-ə
49. Honolulu  hŏn´ə-lōō´lōō
50. Juneau  jōō´nō

| | | | |
|---|---|---|---|
| ă | pat | oi | boy |
| ā | pay | ou | out |
| âr | care | ŏŏ | took |
| ä | father | ōō | boot |
| ĕ | pet | ŭ | cut |
| ē | be | ûr | urge |
| ĭ | pit | th | thin |
| ī | pie | *th* | this |
| îr | pier | hw | which |
| ŏ | pot | zh | vision |
| ō | toe | ə | about |
| ô | paw | | item |

**Stress marks:**
´ (primary);
´ (secondary), as in
**dictionary** (dĭk´shə-nĕr´ē)

# Pronunciation Guide: The 13 provinces and territories of Canada and their capitals (Map #8)

1. Whitehorse, Yukon Territory   wīt´hôrs, yōō´kŏn tĕr´ĭ-tôr´ē
2. Yellowknife, Northwest Territories   yĕl´ō-nīf´, nôrth´wĕst tĕr´ĭ-tôr´ēz
3. Iqualit, Nunavut   ĭk´ə-lĭt´, nən´ə-vŭt´
4. Victoria, British Columbia   vĭk´tôr-ē-ə, brĭt´ĭsh kə-lŭm´bē-ə
5. Edmonton, Alberta   ĕd´mən-tən, ăl-bûr´tə
6. Regina, Saskatchewan   rə-gīn´ə, să-skăch´ə-wän´
7. Winnipeg, Manitoba   wĭn´ə-pĕg´, măn´ĭ-tō´bə
8. Toronto, Ontario   tə-rŏn´tō, ŏn-târ´ē-ō´
9. Quebec, Quebec   kwĭ-bĕk´, kwĭ-bĕk´
10. St. John's, Newfoundland   sānt jŏnz, nōō´fən-lənd
11. Halifax, Nova Scotia   hăl´ə-făks´, nō´və skō´shə
12. Fredericton, New Brunswick   frĕd´rĭc-tən, nōō brŭnz´wĭk
13. Charlottetown, Prince Edward Island   shär´lət-toun´, prĭns ĕd´wərd ī´lənd

24. Ottawa, Canada   ŏt´ə-wä´, kăn´ə-də  (the national capital of Canada)


# Pronunciation Guide: The 8 countries of Mexico and Central America and their capitals (Map #11)

1. Mexico City, Mexico   mĕk´sĭ-kō´ sĭt´ē, mĕk´sĭ-kō´
2. Belmopan, Belize   bĕl´mō-păn´, bə-lēz´
3. Guatemala City, Guatemala   gwä´tə-mä´lə sĭt´ē, gwä´tə-mä´lə
4. Tegucigalpa, Honduras   tə-gōō´sə-găl´pə, hŏn-dōŏr´əs
5. San Salvador, El Salvador   săn săl´və-dôr´, ĕl săl´və-dôr´
6. Managua, Nicaragua   mə-näg´wə, nĭk´ə-rä´gwə
7. San Jose, Costa Rica   săn hō-zā´, kŏs´tə rē´kə
8. Panama, Panama   păn´ə-mä´, păn´ə-mä´

# Pronunciation Guide: Boundary rivers of Mexico and Central America (Map #12)

1. Rio Grande  rē´ō grănd
2. Hondo  hän´dō
3. Coco  kō´kō
4. San Juan  săn wän

# Pronunciation Guide: Boundary rivers of North America (Map #15)

1. Columbia  kə-lŭm´bē-ə
2. Snake  snāk
3. Missouri  mĭ-zŏŏ´rē
4. Mississippi  mĭs´ĭ-sĭp´ē
5. Wabash  wô´băsh´
6. Ohio  ō-hī´ō
7. Ottawa  ŏt´ə-wä
8. Connecticut  kə-nĕt´ĭ-kət
9. Red  rĕd
10. Rio Grande  rē´ō grănd
11. Colorado  kŏl´ə-rä´dō
12. Chattahoochee  chăt´ə-hōō´chē

©1995 Cartesia Software

## Map #1 in the Study of South America: Relative Location

- North America to the northwest
- Africa to the east
- Antarctica to the south
- Asia to the west

- Caribbean Sea to the north.
- Atlantic Ocean to the east
- Antarctic or Southern Ocean to the south
- Pacific Ocean to the west

   The equator passes through Ecuador, Colombia and Brazil, placing South America in both the Northern and Southern Hemispheres. It is in the Western Hemisphere because it is west of the prime meridian.

## Map #2 in the Study of South America: Pretest

Use this map to become familiar with all the countries of South America. It is always fun to take a test before you begin something new so that you can measure your progress as you learn. Take a pretest now and see how many countries of South America you can name at this point. There are 13 countries on this continent and four bodies of water surrounding it. Map #3 will identify the countries and the bodies of water.

Caribbean Sea

NICARAGUA

COSTA RICA

PANAMA

VENEZUELA

GUYANA

SURINAME

FRENCH GUIANA

COLOMBIA

ECUADOR

GALAPAGOS ISLANDS.

PERU

BRAZIL

BOLIVIA

PARAGUAY

CHILE

URUGUAY

ARGENTINA

N
W    E
S

FALKLAND ISLANDS

SOUTH GEORGIA ISLAND

©1995 Cartesia Software

# Map #5 in the Study of South America: Enrichment Activity

There are 13 countries on the South American continent. Do not make the mistake of thinking South America is a country. It is not. It is a continent. Look closely and determine where rivers form boundaries between countries. These natural boundaries are important to note, as they affect the movement of people, goods and ideas. The Amazon Rain Forest is an example of a natural barrier. There are places within this forest that you cannot pass through due to the dense growth of plants. The great height of the Andes also creates a natural barrier. Remember, natural boundaries will be visible to the eye, form a barrier of some sort and be easily recognized. Thus, they make good national and international boundaries. Notice the Falkland Islands to the east of the tip of the continent. They are claimed by England. There are no natural resources and no important cities there. These cold, windy islands are important due to their maritime boundaries. Each country bordered by an ocean is allowed to establish a maritime boundary, usually 12 miles offshore. They have exclusive rights to the fish, minerals and other natural resources found within these waters. Therein lies the importance of the Falkland Islands.

©1995 Cartesia Software

# Map #6 in the Study of South America: Boundary Rivers

1. Rio Meta
2. Rio Orinoco
3. Rio Negro
4. Putumayo

5. Guapore
6. Pilcomayo
7. Rio Paraguay

8. Rio Parana
9. Rio Uruguay
10. Oyapock

11. Maroni
12. Courantyne
13. Ireng

15

1

13

12 11

14

2

3

4

10

9

16

8

5

7

6

N
W E
S

FALKLAND ISLANDS

SOUTH GEORGIA ISLAND

17

©1995 Cartesia Software

# Map #7 in the Study of South America: Map Test

On a clean sheet of paper, list the numbers 1-17. Write the name of each country or body of water beside each corresponding number. Next to the name of each country, write the name of its capital. Be sure to check your spelling. One of the marks of a well educated person is correct spelling. For each name you misspell, please write it ten times correctly, or until you are confident you have mastered the correct spelling.

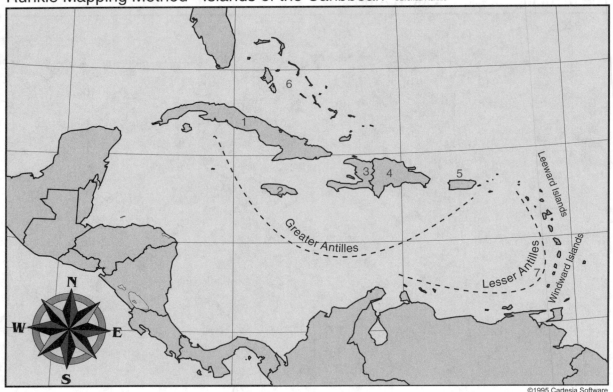

©1995 Cartesia Software

## Map #8 in the Study of South America: Islands of the Caribbean

The West Indies form an archipelago between Florida and South America that separates the Atlantic Ocean from the Caribbean Sea. They were so named by Columbus because they were in the Western Hemisphere. The major islands are:

| | | | |
|---|---|---|---|
| 1. Cuba | 2. Jamaica | 3. Haiti | 4. Dominican Republic |
| 5. Puerto Rico | 6. Bahamas | 7. Lesser Antilles | |

Cuba is the largest island in the Caribbean and the 14th largest island in the world. Once a playground for the rich and famous, Fidel Castro's nation is now suffering severe economic hardships due to its communist policies.

Jamaica, an island discovered by Columbus in 1494, is today a tourist's tropical paradise. Formerly a British colony, it achieved full independence in 1962.

Haiti, a French-speaking republic, is the poorest nation in the Caribbean. It occupies the western third of the island of Hispaniola. When you look at a satellite photograph of the entire island, the Haitian portion is completely denuded of trees and shows terrible erosion due to overgrazing by cattle and goats. Only 45% of the people in Haiti can read and write.

The Dominican Republic occupies the eastern two-thirds of the island of Hispaniola. The capital, Santo Domingo, is the oldest European settlement in the Western Hemisphere. Supposedly, the ashes of Columbus are buried on the island.

Puerto Rico is a self-governing commonwealth in union with the United States. About three times the size of Rhode Island, both Spanish and English are official languages. In 1993 46% of the citizens voted to become the 51st state of the United States, while 48% voted to remain a commonwealth.

The Bahamas are a group of nearly 700 islands in an archipelago extending 590 miles between Florida and Haiti. A member of the British Commonwealth, tourism is the mainstay of the economy. Shallow seas around the islands make this area a haven for pirates and drug smugglers.

The Lesser Antilles include the Windward and Leeward Islands. Windward means exposed to the winds, which are heavy with moisture. Leeward means protected from the winds, resulting in inadequate rainfall. The northern islands are dry, while the southern ones are well watered.

# Learning South America the Easy Way!

There are 13 countries in South America: Venezuela, Colombia (notice the spelling of Colombia), Ecuador, Peru, Chile, Uruguay, Paraguay, Bolivia, Brazil, French Guiana, Suriname, and Guyana. Almost all large cities in South America are along the coastlines of the continent.

Use your Robinson projection to help the students understand the relative location of the South American continent. Point out how most of South America is below the equator, in the Southern Hemisphere, and almost all of South America lies east of Florida. In fact, the eastern bulge of South America is only 1,700 miles from the western bulge of Africa across the Atlantic. Compare that to the 3,500 miles separating New York City from Lisbon, Portugal! Moving to the west and crossing the Pacific, the distance from the western coast of South America to Australia is almost twice as great as from California to Japan! It is also interesting to note that South America is 900 miles south of Florida and only 600 miles north of Antarctica.

Look again at the map and notice that the equator passes through Ecuador, Colombia, and Brazil. The constellations look very different in the Southern Hemisphere. You cannot see the North Star, but you can see the beautiful Southern Cross.

The Andes Mountains extend about 4,500 miles from Colombia and Venezuela at the northern end of the continent all the way to Cape Horn at the southern end. The snow line of the Andes ranges from 4,000 feet in the south to 17,000 feet at the equator. The snow line is the point at which snow stays on the ground year-round. The tree line ranges from 3,000 feet in the south to 12,000 feet at the equator. The tree line indicates the highest elevation at which trees can survive. Above that line it is too cold or has too short a growing season for the trees. Can you figure out why the snow and tree lines are so much higher at the equator than in the south? Think about the direct rays of the sun at the equator.

Have you ever wondered why the people in Brazil speak Portuguese rather than Spanish? Well, in 1493 A.D., Pope Alexander VI decided a dividing line would have to be drawn in order to prevent a war between Spain and Portugal over the wealth in Asia and the Americas. Spain could lay claim to all the land west of approximately 48° W longitude and Portugal could lay claim to all the land east of it. Although the original line barely touched the eastern coast of South America, which had not even been discovered yet, the Treaty of Tordesillas one year later finally determined 51°W longitude would be the dividing line. Thus, Portugal laid claim to the Philippines in the Pacific, which they later traded to Spain for all of Brazil! And that is why they speak Portuguese rather than Spanish in Brazil!

Columbus had decided in 1498 that South America was a true continent but did not make any territorial claims. Amerigo Vespucci also sailed by but made no claims. Keep in mind that the Spanish only wanted the riches of the land and to conquer natives to do the work for them. The eastern coast of South America offered neither riches nor slaves.

It is easy to learn the thirteen countries of South America using two mnemonics, one for the western countries, and another for the eastern and interior countries. Notice that the first letter of each word on the mnemonic matches the first letter of the name of a country.

## Venezuela, Colombia, Ecuador, Peru, Chile

These five countries all lie on the western side of the continent. The mnemonic I use to remember them is:

| | |
|---|---|
| Very | **V**enezuela |
| Cold | **C**olombia |
| Elephants | **E**cuador |
| Prefer | **P**eru |
| Chile | **C**hile |

Venezuela is the wealthiest country in South America. It was a founding member of OPEC, the oil-exporting cartel that determines the world's price of oil. Oil brings in 90 cents out of every dollar in Venezuela. Lake Maracaibo, the largest lake in South America, has over 200 oil wells. Lake Maracaibo is actually a bay. The world's highest waterfall is Angel Falls in Venezuela. It is 3,212 feet high compared to Niagara Falls at 167 feet!

Colombia has coasts along the Caribbean and the Pacific. It is famous for emeralds, tin and refining much of the world's cocaine. Cocaine is refined from the leaves of the coca plant. Don't confuse *coca* with the *cocoa* plant from which we get chocolate!

Ecuador claims the Galapagos Islands, home to the huge, long-lived Galapagos turtles. The country is often victim to volcanic activity and earthquakes.

Peru is the world's largest grower of coca, from which cocaine is refined. Peru was the center of the ancient Inca empire. Machu Picchu is the site of an ancient Inca city, discovered in 1911.

The Atacama Desert in Chile is one of the driest places on earth, yet it averages a temperature of 65°F year-round due to the elevation. Chile is only 110 miles wide from east to west, but is 2,650 miles long from north to south.

## Argentina, Uruguay, Paraguay, Bolivia, Brazil, French Guiana, Suriname, Guyana

I have two different mnemonics for remembering these countries:

| | | |
|---|---|---|
| **A**ll | **A**rgentina | Are |
| **U**rban | **U**ruguay | Unearthly |
| **P**eople | **P**araguay | Parasites |
| **B**etter | **B**olivia | Boiled |
| **B**e | **B**razil | Better |
| **F**riendly **G**irls | **F**rench **G**uiana | Fresh Ground |
| **S**mart | **S**uriname | Salted |
| **G**uys | **G**uyana | Good? |

Mnemonics are just silly, nonsensical ways to remember things. Friendly girls and fresh ground both seem to go with French Guiana. I chose guys to emphasize the spelling of Guyana. Both of these mnemonics are silly, so take your pick!

Cowboys in Argentina are called *gauchos* and wear split skirts! No Levis for them!

Here is an interesting problem. The Falkland Islands lie 300 miles east of the Strait of Magellan. They are also known as the Islas Malvinas. Argentina, France and Spain have tried to claim them even though British rule was established there in 1833. In fact, Argentina went to war with England in 1982 in an attempt to gain these windswept islands. In 1962, the British Antarctic Territory was created to include all of the area south of 60° S latitude and 80° W longitude. This region will become even more important as natural resources are discovered on Antarctica and along the seafloor surrounding the islands. In 1914, the British defeated the Germans in a naval battle near the Falklands, thus establishing the military importance of this region. The Falklands are now an important British base.

Bolivia, one of only two landlocked countries on the continent, is the poorest and most politically unstable of all the South American countries. Lake Titicaca, the world's highest navigable lake, is on the border between Bolivia and Peru.

Brazil touches every South America country except Ecuador and Chile. It is also the largest producer of coffee. Did you know that the entire contiguous 48 United States could fit inside Brazil and have room left over? Brazil is so big that the northeastern part identifies itself with Portugal and the Caribbean nations and looks upon the southern part as a foreign nation!

Brazil's capital, Brasilia, is in the south and sends its unwanted poor north into the Amazon basin to farm. The soil is so poor in Amazonia that after two or three years, the land cannot support any crops and the people move on, using slash-and-burn agriculture. That means they cut down all the trees and burn everything to provide fertilizer for the crops. When they move on, the land erodes and becomes useless. It is estimated the Amazon Rain Forest will disappear by the year 2020 if the current rate of destruction continues. These forests are vital sources of free oxygen in our atmosphere! Forests also act as the garbage collectors of our atmosphere as they absorb harmful carbon dioxide. This is a very complex economic problem though, so let's not pass judgement until we study the whole region.

The Amazon River is shorter than the Nile. Some put the length of the river at 4,100 miles compared to 4,160 miles of the Nile. However, in just one day the Amazon discharges more water into the Atlantic Ocean than New York City uses in 9 years, or enough to meet the needs of all households in the U.S. for five months! That is a lot of water! Marajo, the world's largest depositional island (an island created by silt dropped by a river) is at the mouth of the Amazon.

The only part of the continent not settled by the Spanish or Portuguese were the Guianas. Explorers only saw the forests growing right down to the ocean and a hot, humid climate. No slaves, no natural wealth, so they were simply not interested. Along came the Dutch in 1621 who claimed Dutch Guiana, now called Suriname. The French claimed French Guiana, which they still claim, and the British claimed British Guiana, now known as Guyana. So, at one time, the entire continent of South America was claimed by European nations.

# Pronunciation Guide: The 13 countries of South America and their capitals (Maps #3 and #4)

1. Caracus, Venezuela  kə-rä´kəs, vĕn´ə-zwā´lə
2. Bogota, Colombia  bō´gə-tä´, kə-lŭm´bē-ə
3. Quito, Ecuador  kē´tō, ĕk´wə-dôr´
4. Lima, Peru  lē´mə, pə-rōō´
5. Santiago, Chile  săn´tē-ä´gō, chĭl´ē
6. Buenos Aires, Argentina  bwā´nəs âr´ēz, är´jən-tē´nə
7. Montevideo, Uruguay  mŏn´tə-vĭ-dā´ō, yŏŏr´ə-gwī´
8. Asuncion, Paraguay  ä-sōōn´syôn´, păr´ə-gwī´
9. La Paz and Sucre, Bolivia  lə-päz´ and sōō´krā, bə-lĭv´ē-ə
10. Brasilia, Brazil  brə-zĭl´yə, brə-zĭl´
11. Cayenne, French Guiana  kī-ĕn´, frĕnch gē-ăn´ə
12. Paramaribo, Suriname  păr´ə-măr´ə-bō´, sû´rə-nä´mə
13. Georgetown, Guyana  jôrj´toun´, gī-ăn´ə

# Pronunciation Guide: Boundary Rivers of South America (Map #6)

1. Rio Meta  rē´ō  mä´tə
2. Rio Orinoco  rē´ō  ôr´ə-nō´kō
3. Rio Negro  rē´ō  nä´grō
4. Putumayo  pōō´tə-mī´ō
5. Guapore  gwä´pə-rā´
6. Pilcomayo  pĭl´kō-mä´yō
7. Rio Paraguay  rē´ō  păr´ə-gwī´
8. Rio Parana  rē´ō  păr´ə-nä´
9. Rio Uruguay  rē´ō  yŏŏr´ə-gwī´
10. Oyapock  ô-yə-pôk´
11. Maroni  mə-rō´nē
12. Courantyne  kōr´ən-tīn´
13. Ireng  ī´renj

# Pronunciation Guide: Caribbean Islands (Map #8)

1. Cuba  kyōō´bə
2. Jamaica  jə-mā´kə
3. Haiti  hā´tē
4. Dominican Republic  də-mĭn´ĭ-kən rĭ-pŭb´lĭk
5. Puerto Rico  pwĕr´tə rē´kō
6. Bahamas  bə-hä´məz
7. Lesser Antilles  lĕs´ər  ăn-tĭl´ēz

| ă pat | oi boy |
|---|---|
| ā pay | ou out |
| âr care | ŏŏ tŏŏk |
| ä father | ōō bōōt |
| ĕ pet | ŭ cut |
| ē be | ûr urge |
| ĭ pit | th thin |
| ī pie | *th* this |
| îr pier | hw which |
| ŏ pot | zh vision |
| ō toe | ə about |
| ô paw | item |

**Stress marks:**
´ (primary);
´ (secondary), as in
**dictionary** (dĭk´shə-nĕr´ē)

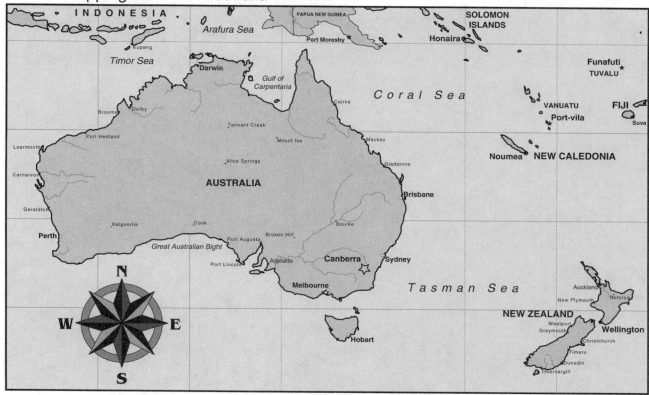

©1995 Cartesia Software

# Map #1 in the Study of Australia: Relative Location

- Asia to the north
- Africa to the west
- South America to the east

- Timor Sea to the northwest
- Arafura Sea to the north
- Coral Sea to the northeast

- Tasman Sea to the southeast
- Pacific Ocean to the east
- Indian Ocean to the South and the west

Australia is the smallest of the continents, yet the world's sixth largest country. It is comparable to the United States in land size. It is the lowest and flattest continent. It is the driest and least populated of all the continents excluding Antarctica. Australia is entirely in the Southern Hemisphere. Two-thirds of Australia is covered by the Western Plateau. This area has no trees or rivers and is covered with sand. The Great Dividing Range separates the dry interior from the fertile east coast. Australia is divided into eight territories and states. They are Western Australia, Northern Territory, South Australia, Queensland, New South Wales, Victoria, Australian Capital Territory, and Tasmania. Tasmania is the island just off the southern coast. The Australian Capital Territory is similar to Washington D.C. Australia's capital, Canberra, is located there. The largest city is Sydney, located on the eastern coast. New Zealand is not part of Australia. It is a separate country located 1300 miles (2092 km) off the southeastern coast.

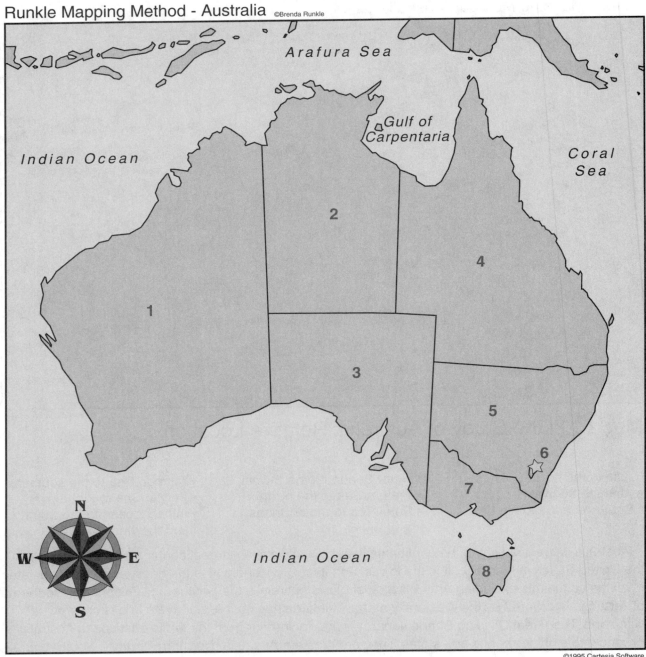

Map #2 in the Study of Australia: The 8 Territories and States

1. Western Australia
2. Northern Territory
3. South Australia
4. Queensland

5. New South Wales
6. Australian Capital Territory, Canberra
7. Victoria
8. Tasmania

Arafura Sea

Gulf of Carpentaria

Indian Ocean

Coral Sea

Northern Territory

Western Australia

Queensland

South Australia

New South Wales

Victoria

Indian Ocean

Tasmania

N
W E
S

©1995 Cartesia Software

# Map #3 in the Study of Australia: Rivers

Most of Australia is dry and arid, but there are a few major rivers.

1. Murray River    2. Lachlan River    3. Darling River

# Learning Australia the Easy Way!

The continent of Australia lies in a region which includes Oceania. Many new textbooks include Australia as part of Oceania and not even refer to it individually! For our purposes, though, we will recognize Australia as a continent country. Oceania will include the Pacific islands of the Federated States of Micronesia, Fiji, Marshall Islands, New Zealand, Papua New Guinea, Samoa, Solomon Islands and Vanuatu.

Australia is the smallest of the continents and the only one that can claim to be an island continent. It is also the only continent that is one country. There are six states and two territories. Tasmania, the little island to the south, is an Australian state and has about half of Australia's potential hydroelectric power. Remnants of huge giant squid have been found in Bass Strait between Tasmania and Victoria.

Remember, Australia is below the equator, placing it in the Southern Hemisphere, so the winds blow counterclockwise. That means that the heaviest rainfall is along the eastern coasts. The Great Dividing Range creates an orographic effect, or rain shadow, making the interior extremely dry. There are three distinct deserts in the interior of the continent: the Great Victoria Desert to the south, Gibson Desert in the middle, and the Great Sandy Desert to the north. Look closely at the location of the rivers and you will notice they are mostly around the edges of the continent. The highest elevation is Mt. Kosciusko, at 7,310 feet, in the Great Dividing Range along the east coast.

The northwest parts are hot and dry, while the northeast has heavy rainfall, with jungles on the Cape York Peninsula. The Murray River rises in New South Wales and flows 1,600 miles northwest to the Indian Ocean, forming part of the boundary between Victoria and New South Wales. At approximately 142° E, the Murray joins with the Darling River. Further east, at about 143° N 13´E, It joins with the Lachlan River. Shallow during the dry season, the Murray has numerous sand bars at its mouth, preventing entry of large ships.

Because of its isolation as a continent, there are many animals in Australia that are not found anywhere else on our planet. They include kangaroos, koalas, platypuses, dingos (wild dogs), Tasmanian devils (raccoon-like marsupials), wombats (bear-like marsupials), and barking and frilled lizards!

Australia is the world's leading producer of wool and among the top exporters of beef, lamb and wheat. The wine industry is gaining worldwide recognition. There are 126 million sheep, 27 million cattle and 2.7 million pigs on the continent!

# Pronunciation Guide: Relative location of Australia (Map #1)

Timor Sea   tē´môr sē
Arafura Sea   ä´rə-fōō´rə sē
Coral Sea   kôr´əl sē
Tasman Sea   tăz´mən sē

# Pronunciation Guide: The 8 states and territories of Australia (Map #2)

1. Western Australia   wĕs´tərn ô-strāl´yə
2. Northern Territory   nôr*th*´ərn tĕr´ĭ-tôr´ēz
3. South Australia   south ô-strāl´yə
4. Queensland   kwēnz´lənd
5. New South Wales   nōō south wālz
6. Australian Capital Territory, Canberra   ô-strāl´yən kăp´ĭ-təl tĕr´ĭ-tôr´ē, kăn´bĕr-ə
7. Victoria   vĭk´tôr-ē-ə
8. Tasmania   tăz-mā´nē-ə

# Runkle Mapping Method - Oceania ©Brenda Runkle

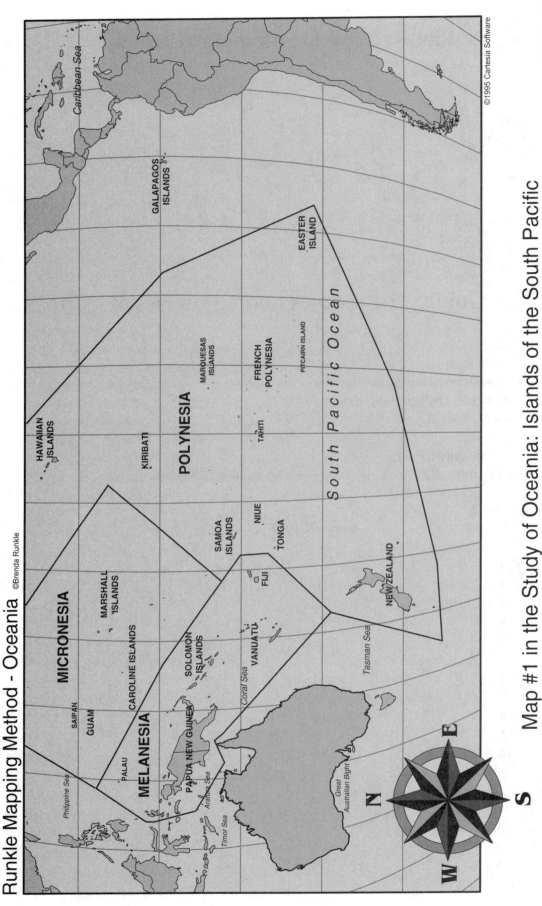

©1995 Cartesia Software

S    Map #1 in the Study of Oceania: Islands of the South Pacific

Notice most of the islands fall within three groupings or collective names.
Micronesia means small islands (micro = small, nesia = islands).
Melanesia means black islands (mela = black, nesia = islands).
Polynesia means many islands (poly = many, nesia = islands).

# Learning Oceania the Easy Way!

Oceania is the collective name for the lands of the central and south Pacific Ocean, including Micronesia, Melanesia and Polynesia. These divisions are based upon the race and customs of the native peoples as well as geography.

Although there are some large islands, altogether the islands of Oceania cover less land than the state of Alaska. New Guinea is the largest island, with New Zealand's two main islands second and third largest. Together these three islands equal more than 80% of the total land area of the Pacific Islands.

## Micronesia

Micronesia (micro = small, nesia = island) is officially defined as a division of Oceania in the W Pacific that is east of the Philippines, north of the equator and south of Japan.

The Federated States of Micronesia are about four times the size of Washington, D.C., with 271 square miles in land area. These small islands are spread out over 1,800 miles across an archipelago of the Caroline Islands, in the larger island group of Micronesia. After WWII they were placed under a trusteeship with the United States, which means we guaranteed their safety at all times, especially during war. The trusteeship was officially dissolved in 1990. Guam is the largest island in Micronesia.

The Marshall Islands consist of 31 coral atolls of the Ratak (Sunrise) and Ralik (Sunset) chains in the western Pacific. The total land area is only 70 square miles. There is a constitutional government in free association with the U.S. The largest export used to be copra, dried coconut meat! Bikini and Enewetak atolls were used for nuclear testing.

## Melanesia

Melanesia is the collective name for the islands in the southwest Pacific that are northeast of Australia and south of the equator. The islands were named Melanesia (*mela* = black, *nesia* = island) for their black inhabitants.

The Solomon Islands are a group of 14 rugged volcanic islands east of Papua New Guinea. They have a parliamentary democracy within the Commonwealth of Nations. So, although they gained their independence July 7, 1978, Queen Elizabeth remains the Head of State. The Solomon Islands sell tuna-fishing rights within their territorial waters, which gives them a favorable balance of payments. Guadalcanal lies within this group and was the site of terrible battles in WWII.

Vanuatu, formerly known as the New Hebrides, is a chain of 12 principal islands and 60 smaller ones slightly larger than Connecticut. All are volcanic, rugged, and heavily forested. Some peaks exceed 6,000 feet. They were allies of the Free French during World War II and escaped Japanese occupation. They were granted independence in 1980 and membership in the British Commonwealth.

Fiji has more than 300 islands, only 100 of which are inhabited. Slightly smaller than New Jersey, it became a crown colony in 1874. In 1879 large numbers of indentured Indian workerswere brought in to work on the sugar plantations and finally outnumbered the native Fijis. The government formed in 1994 guarantees a majority of seats for ethnic Fijians in the national legislature.

## Polynesia

Polynesia means many islands (poly = many, nesia = island). There are thousands of islands in this group stretching all the way from Midway Island in the north to New Zealand in the south 5,000 miles away. Easter Island, the easternmost island, is more than 4,000 miles east of New Zealand. Many of the islands are coral atolls, while others, such as the Hawaiian Islands, are volcanic.

Western Samoa consists of two large and seven small islands equaling the size of Rhode Island. There is an independent country of Western Samoa and an American Samoa, as a result of partitioning between Germany and the United States in 1899. New Zealand administered Western Samoa until 1959. Independence was granted in 1962. Tourism is the largest source of income.

## New Zealand

New Zealand is an independent member of the British Commonwealth. There are two main islands, each of which is mountainous and hilly. South Isle is the largest island, with 15 peaks over 10,000 feet covered with glaciers. Fertile plains line the east coast, especially the Canterbury Plains. The center of North Isle is a volcanic plateau. However, there is no good farmland on the island, making it suitable only for grazing of sheep and dairy farming.

Here are some facts to help you visualize the size of the islands making up the country of New Zealand: South Island has 58,384 sq. mi.; North Island, 44,702 sq. mi.; Stewart Island, 674 sq. mi.; Chatham Islands, 372 sq. mi.; and there are several groups of even smaller islands. Since 1923, New Zealand has administered 160,000 square miles of Antarctica known as Ross Dependency.

## Papua New Guinea

The island of New Guinea, the world's second largest island, is divided into two countries. Papua occupies the eastern half of the island and also claims about 600 nearby islands. The center of the island is mountainous, with dense forests and lowland coastal areas. There are 715 indigenous languages, with pidgin English spoken widely. Queen Elizabeth is the head of the parliamentary democracy.

The rest of the island of New Guinea belongs to Indonesia. The western part of the island, formerly known as Irian Jaya, joined with Indonesia in 1963.

How many of you have read *Mutiny on the Bounty* by Charles Nordhoff and James Hall? This is a fascinating true story about the mutiny led by Christian Fletcher against Lieutenant Bligh. After the sailors took over the ship and set "Captain" Bligh on his merry way, they sailed to Tahiti where they picked up 6 men and 12 women. They then sailed to Pitcairn Island in the South Pacific, where they settled in 1790 and lived undiscovered until 1808. However, life was not at all peaceful. There were more men than women, which led to dreadful quarrels and fights. After several years only one mutineer was still alive! In 1831, drought forced the survivors to move to Tahiti, then on to Norfolk Island. A few managed to return to Pitcairn Island, where all today's inhabitants are descendants of the mutinous sailors from the Bounty.

An interesting note is that Norfolk Island, located 930 miles ENE of Sydney, Australia, with 13.3 square miles in area, has fertile soil suitable for citrus fruits, coffee and bananas. Many of the 2,209 inhabitants are also descendants of the Bounty mutineers.

# Pronunciation Guide: Oceania

Bikini  bĭ-kē′nē
Caroline Islands  kăr′ə-līn′ ī′ləndz
Easter Island  ē′stər ī′lənd
Enewetak  ĕn′ĭ-wē′täk′
Fiji  fē′jē
Guadalcanal  gwŏd′l-kə-năl′
Guam  gwäm
Marshall Islands  mär′shəl ī′ləndz
Melanesia  mĕl′ə-nē′zhə
Micronesia  mī′krō-nē′zhə
Midway Island  mĭd′wā ī′lənd
New Zealand  nōō zē′lənd
Norfolk Island  nôr′fək ī′lənd
Oceania  ō′shē-ăn′ē-ə
Papua New Guinea  pä′pōō-ä′ nōō gĭn′ē
Pitcairn Island  pĭt′kârn′ ī′lənd
Polynesia  pŏl′ə-nē′zhə
Ralik Chain  rä′lĭk chān
Ratak  rä′täk′ chān
Solomon Islands  sŏl′ə-mən ī′ləndz
Tahiti  tə-hē′tē′
Vanuatu  vä′nōō-ä′tōō
Western Samoa  wĕst′ərn sə-mō′ə

# Runkle Mapping Method ©Brenda Runkle

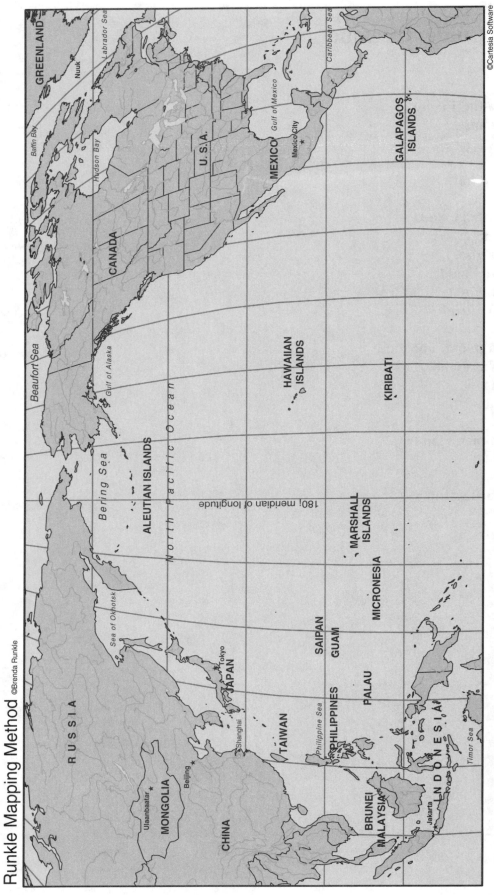

©Cartesia Software

# Islands of the North Pacific

The Galapagos Islands belong to Ecuador. They are most famous as the home of the huge long-lived giant tortoise, now an endangered specie. These islands are of volcanic origin.

The Aleutian Islands are an island arc formed by subduction, as the Pacific plate moves under the North American plate. They separate the Bering Sea from the Pacific Ocean.

Runkle Mapping Method ©Brenda Runkle

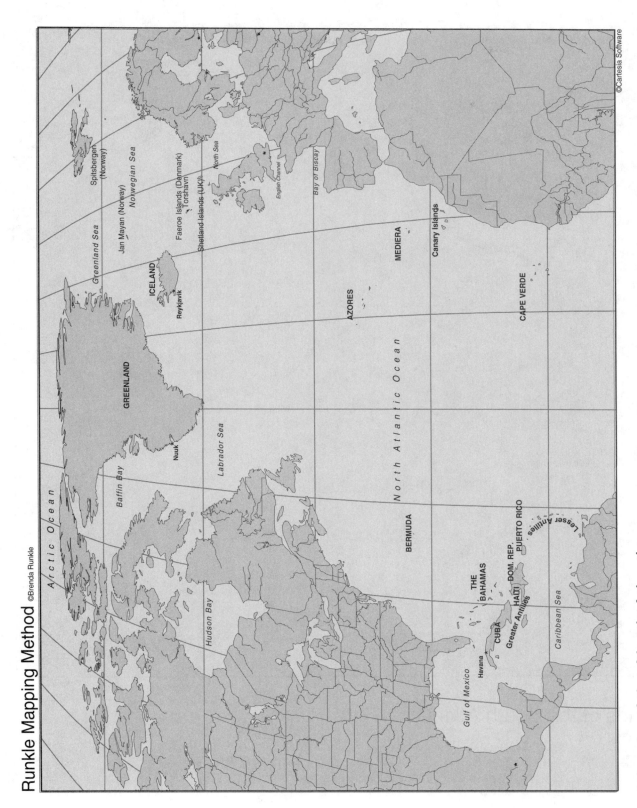

Islands of the North Atlantic

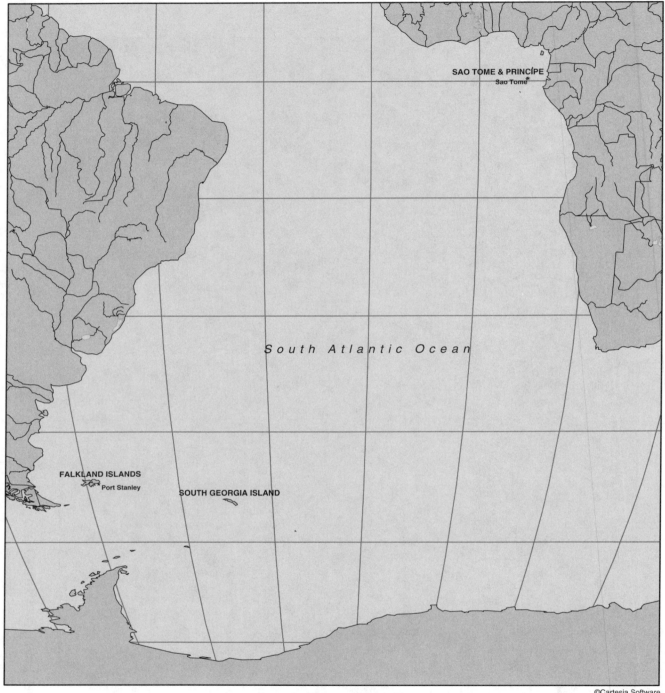

SAO TOME & PRINCÍPE
Sao Tome

*South Atlantic Ocean*

FALKLAND ISLANDS
Port Stanley

SOUTH GEORGIA ISLAND

# Islands of the South Atlantic

Runkle Mapping Method - Europe Centered World Map ©Brenda Runkle

Winkel Tripel

©Cartesia Software

165 E
150 E
135 E
90 W
75 E
60 E
45 E
0
15 S
30 S
45 S
60 S
15 W
30 W
45 W
60 W
75 W
90 W
105 W
120 W
135 W
150 W
165 W
75 N
60 N

Runkle Mapping Method -North America Centered World Map ©Brenda Runkle

©Cartesia Software

Winkel Tripel

# Runkle Mapping Method - Africa  ©Brenda Runkle

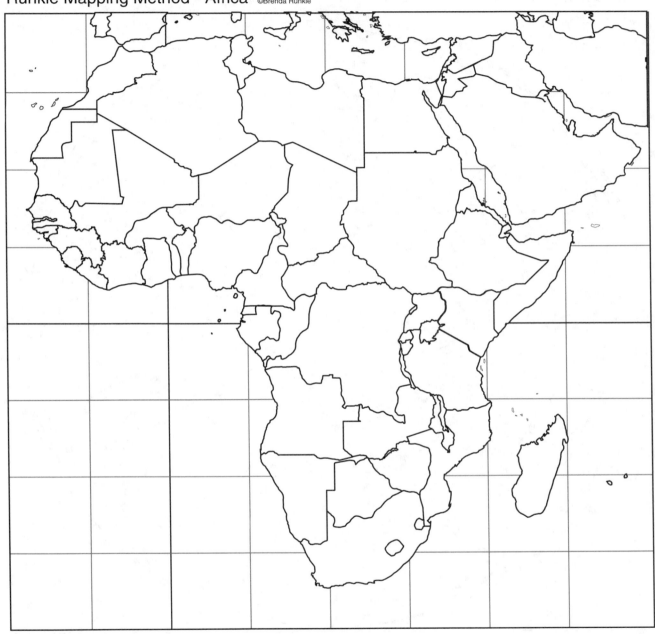

# Runkle Mapping Method - Antarctica ©Brenda Runkle

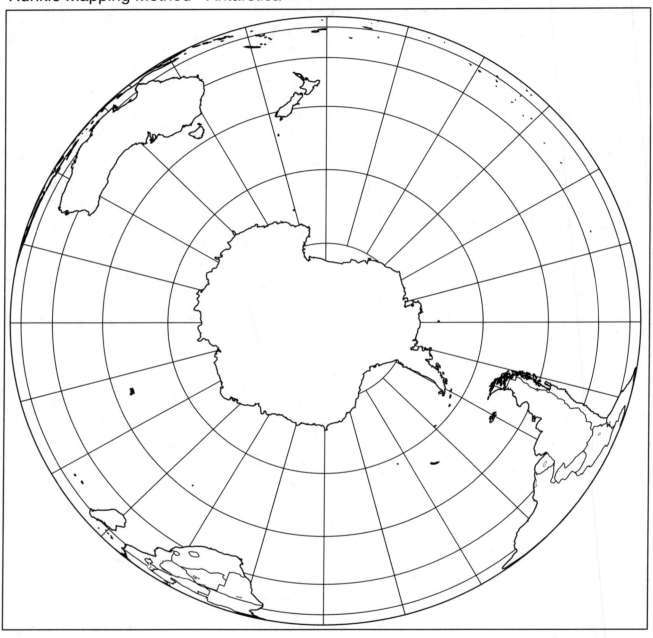

# Runkle Mapping Method - Europe ©Brenda Runkle

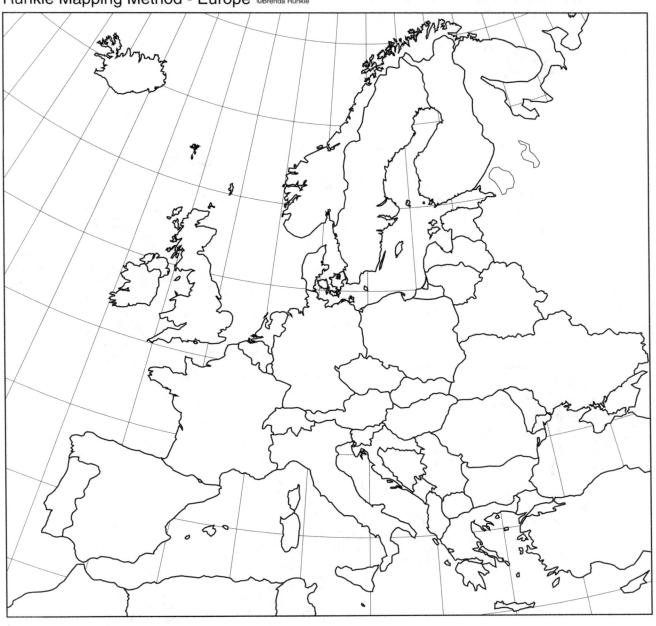

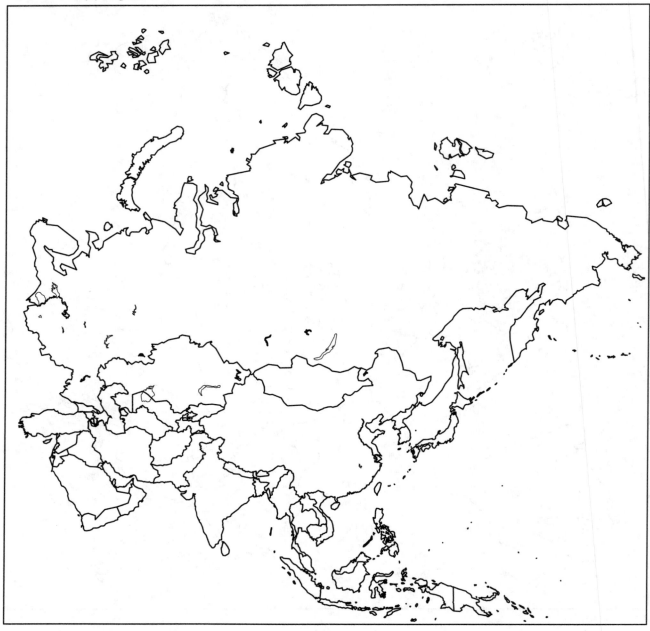

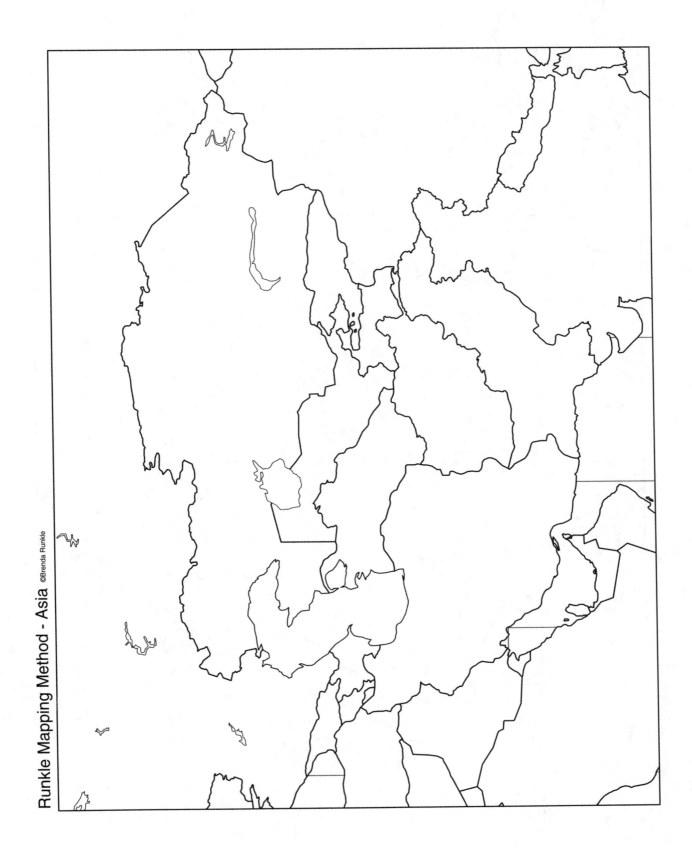

Runkle Mapping Method - Asia ©Brenda Runkle

113

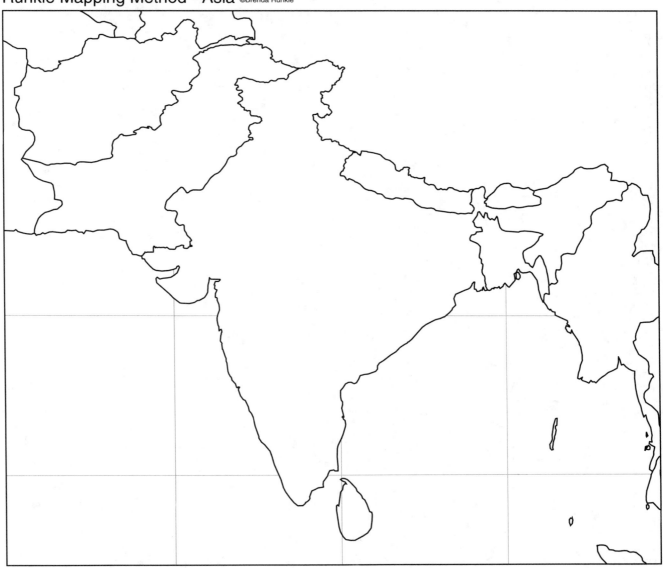

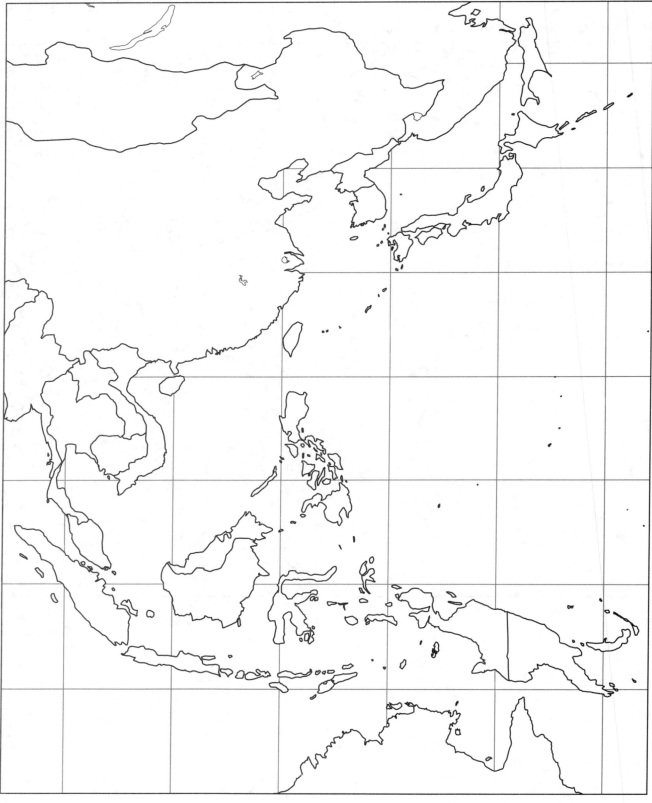

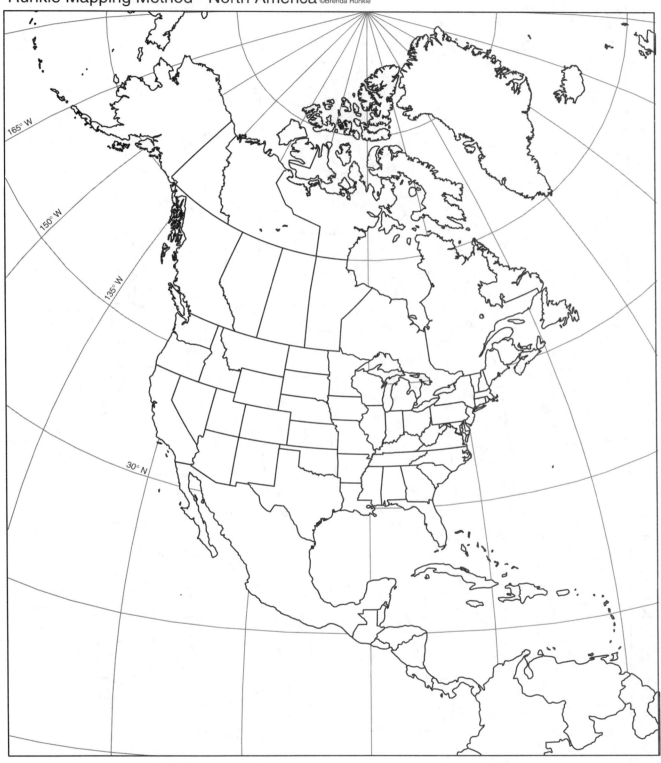

165° W

150° W

135° W

30° N

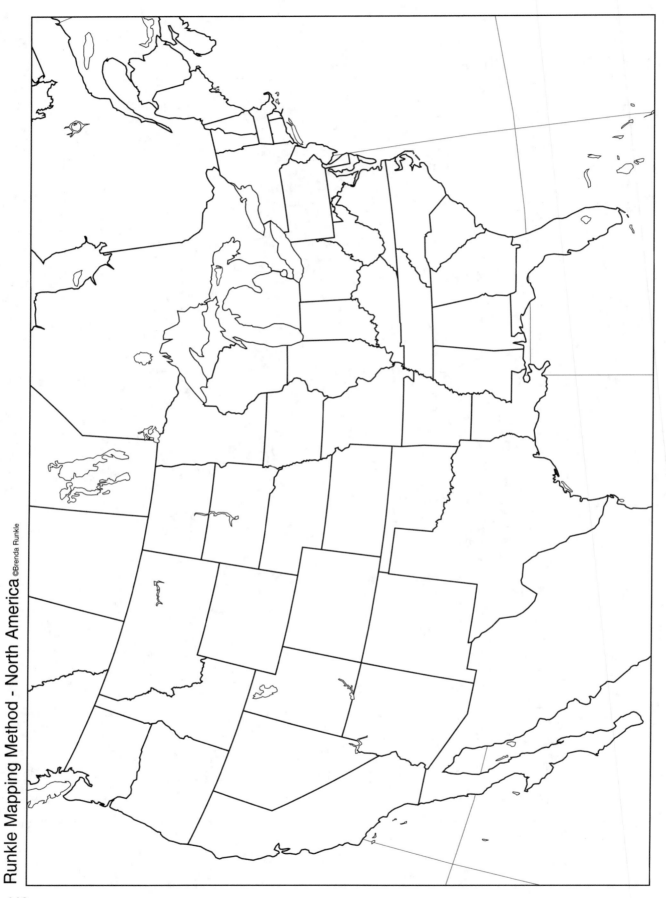

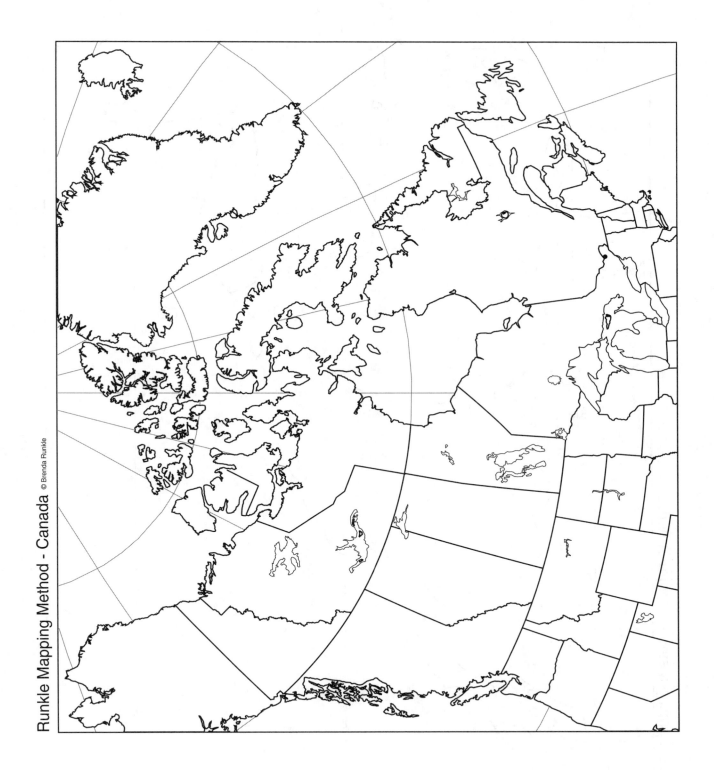

Runkle Mapping Method - Canada © Brenda Runkle

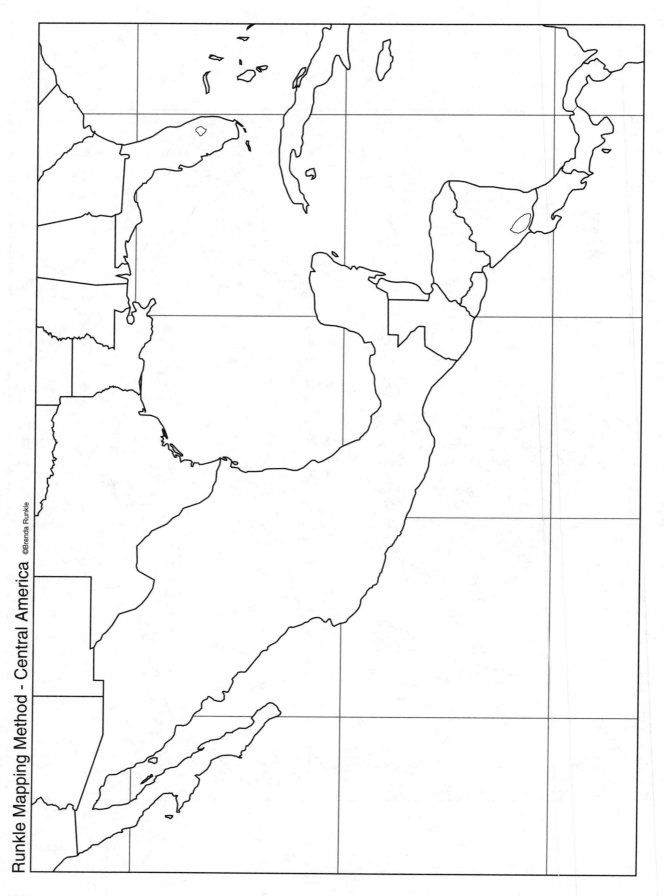